UNIT 4 Patterns in the Sky

Discovering Space

McGraw Hill Wright Group

The McGraw-Hill Companies

www.WrightGroup.com

Printed in USA.

Send all inquiries to:
Wright Group/McGraw-Hill
P.O. Box 812960
Chicago, IL 60681

ISBN 978-0-07-656410-1
MHID 0-07-656410-X

4 5 6 7 8 9 DOC 16 15 14 13 12 11

Contents

Digital 21

My Home Page

ebook

online coach

Why do people study space?

Have you ever looked into the night sky and wondered about it? What are the stars made of? Where did they come from? Over the centuries, people have come up with many ideas about the night sky. Some of these ideas are being changed as scientists learn more.

Focus Questions

Selection 1

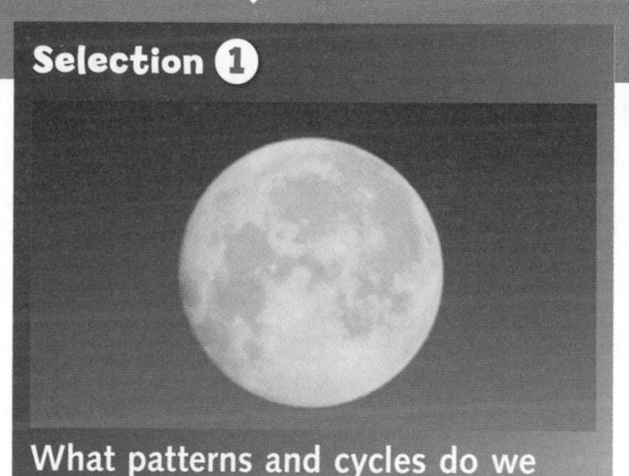

What patterns and cycles do we find in space?

Selection 2

How did people of the past explain objects in the night sky?

Selection 3

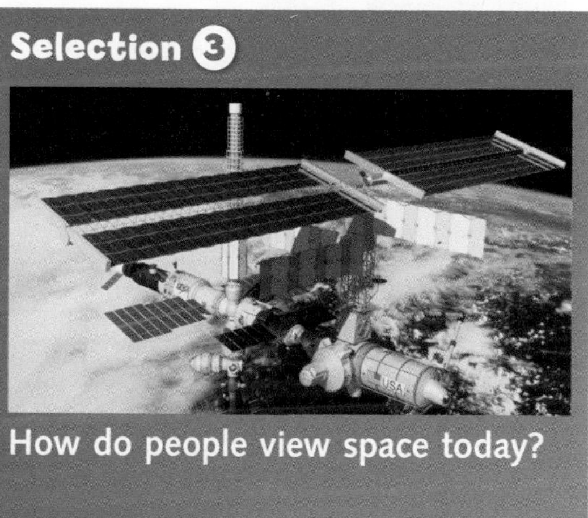

How do people view space today?

Selection 4

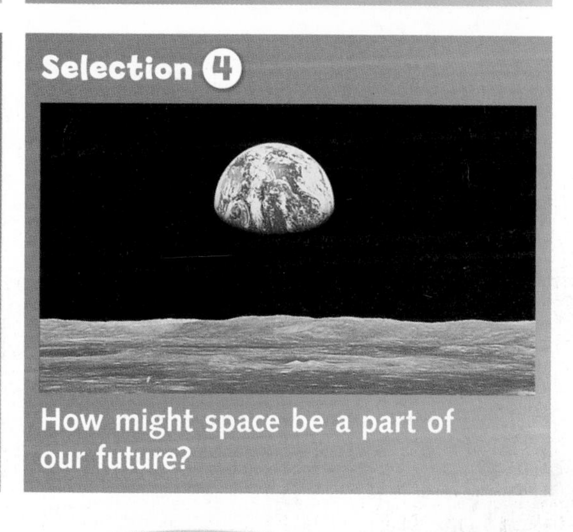

How might space be a part of our future?

online coach

What patterns and cycles do we find in space? Preview pages 6–27. Then read *William Herschel: Astronomer* to find out.

William Herschel Astronomer

by Jana Martin • Illustrated by Leah Palmer Preiss

Sir William Herschel (1738–1822) is thought of as one of the greatest astronomers of his time. An astronomer is someone who studies space, planets, and the stars. Herschel worked for years as a musician, composer, and music teacher. But he spent every free moment studying the night sky.

Before Herschel, the only planets people knew of were those they could see with their own eyes. Herschel was the first person in recorded history to discover a planet. With the aid of a **telescope**, he was able to see the planet Uranus.

Herschel built many telescopes to see deep into the night sky. He wanted the best tools possible to observe, or study, the sky.

Herschel's sister Caroline worked with him. She helped keep records of his observations. She also did calculations, or math work. Together they made a list of some 2,500 objects in the night sky.

Early Life

Herschel was born on November 15, 1738. He was born in a part of Germany called Hanover. His full name was Friedrich Wilhelm Herschel. His father was a musician in the army band.

Music was a highly valued job in the 1700s, so Herschel too became a musician. He played the oboe, an instrument like the clarinet. He joined his father in the band. His family loved learning and studying. Encouraged by his father, Herschel spent years learning to make a living as a musician. He studied the math, or numbers, behind music's notes, scales, and rhythms. Later he would use math to learn about objects he saw in the night sky.

oboe

In 1757 Herschel moved to England. He changed his name from Wilhelm to William. There he began his career in music. He taught students weekly and wrote music of his own. He also became the organist and conductor at the popular Octagon Church in the city of Bath.

A Brother-and-Sister Team

In 1772 Herschel invited his sister, Caroline, to join him in Bath. Caroline left her parents' home and went to England.

Herschel gave Caroline singing and mathematics lessons. She became a very good singer. She began to sing **professionally**. She was even invited to sing in other cities.

Herschel read books about astronomy that fascinated him. Caroline was also interested in new ideas, just like her brother. The brother-and-sister team would study the sky when they were not working on music.

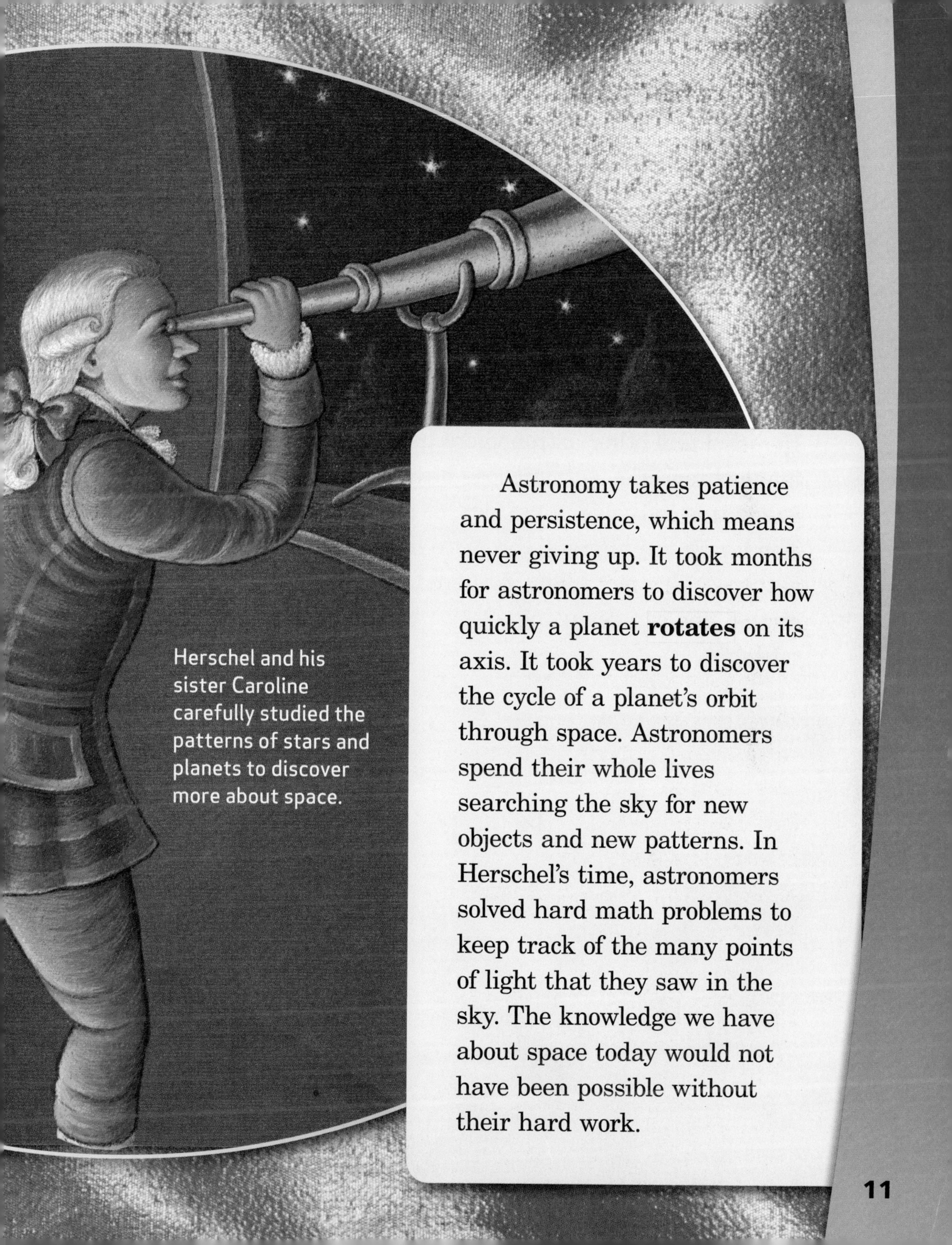

Herschel and his sister Caroline carefully studied the patterns of stars and planets to discover more about space.

Astronomy takes patience and persistence, which means never giving up. It took months for astronomers to discover how quickly a planet **rotates** on its axis. It took years to discover the cycle of a planet's orbit through space. Astronomers spend their whole lives searching the sky for new objects and new patterns. In Herschel's time, astronomers solved hard math problems to keep track of the many points of light that they saw in the sky. The knowledge we have about space today would not have been possible without their hard work.

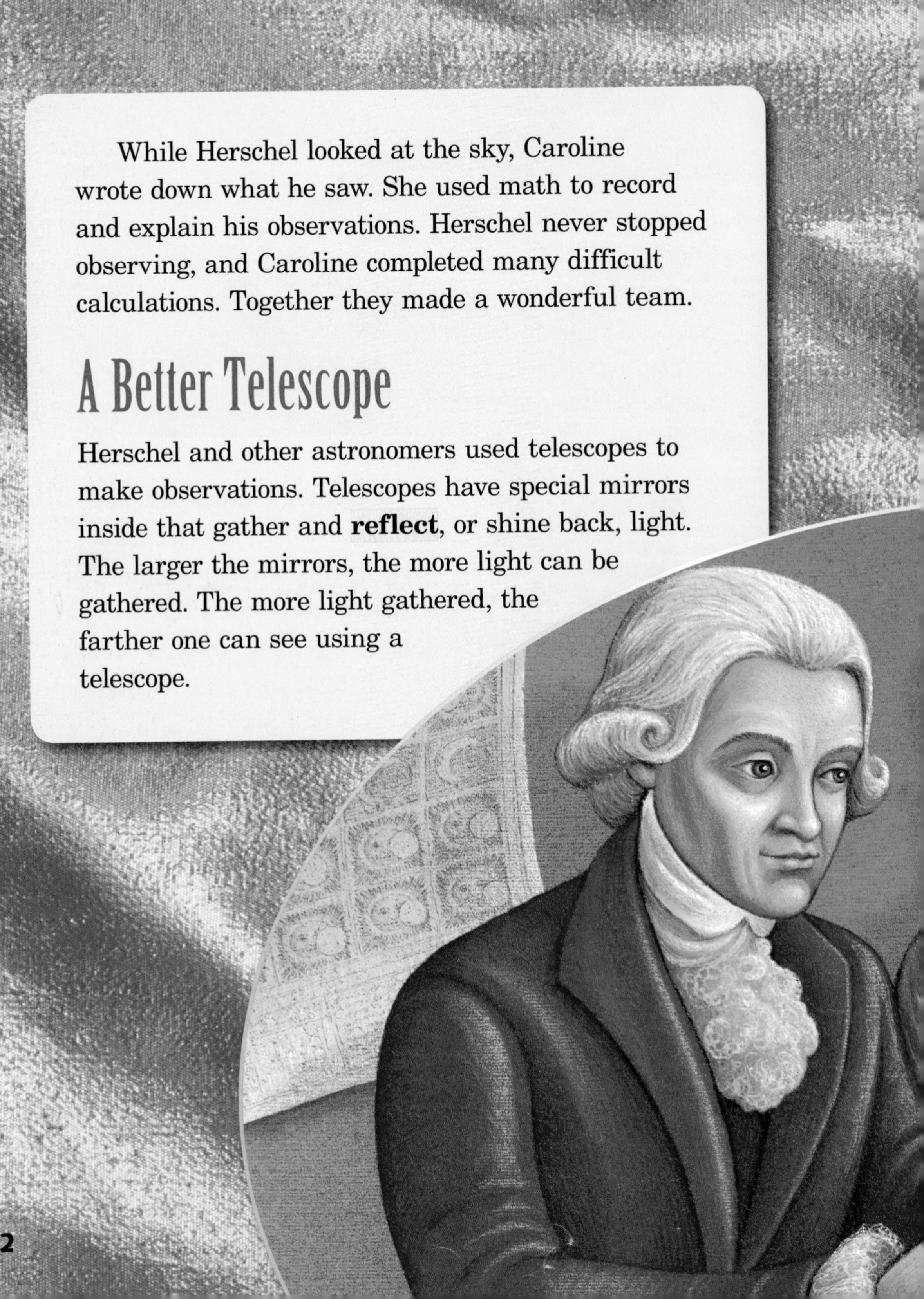

While Herschel looked at the sky, Caroline wrote down what he saw. She used math to record and explain his observations. Herschel never stopped observing, and Caroline completed many difficult calculations. Together they made a wonderful team.

A Better Telescope

Herschel and other astronomers used telescopes to make observations. Telescopes have special mirrors inside that gather and **reflect**, or shine back, light. The larger the mirrors, the more light can be gathered. The more light gathered, the farther one can see using a telescope.

Many astronomers in Herschel's time used telescopes to learn about the sun, the moon, and Earth. But Herschel wanted to discover more. There was no telescope with a mirror large enough for Herschel to look far out into the night sky. He learned everything he could about building telescopes and making his own mirrors. Helped by Caroline, he began to **grind** telescope mirrors out of copper, tin, and other metals. Finally he succeeded in making mirrors that were large enough and exact enough to look farther into space.

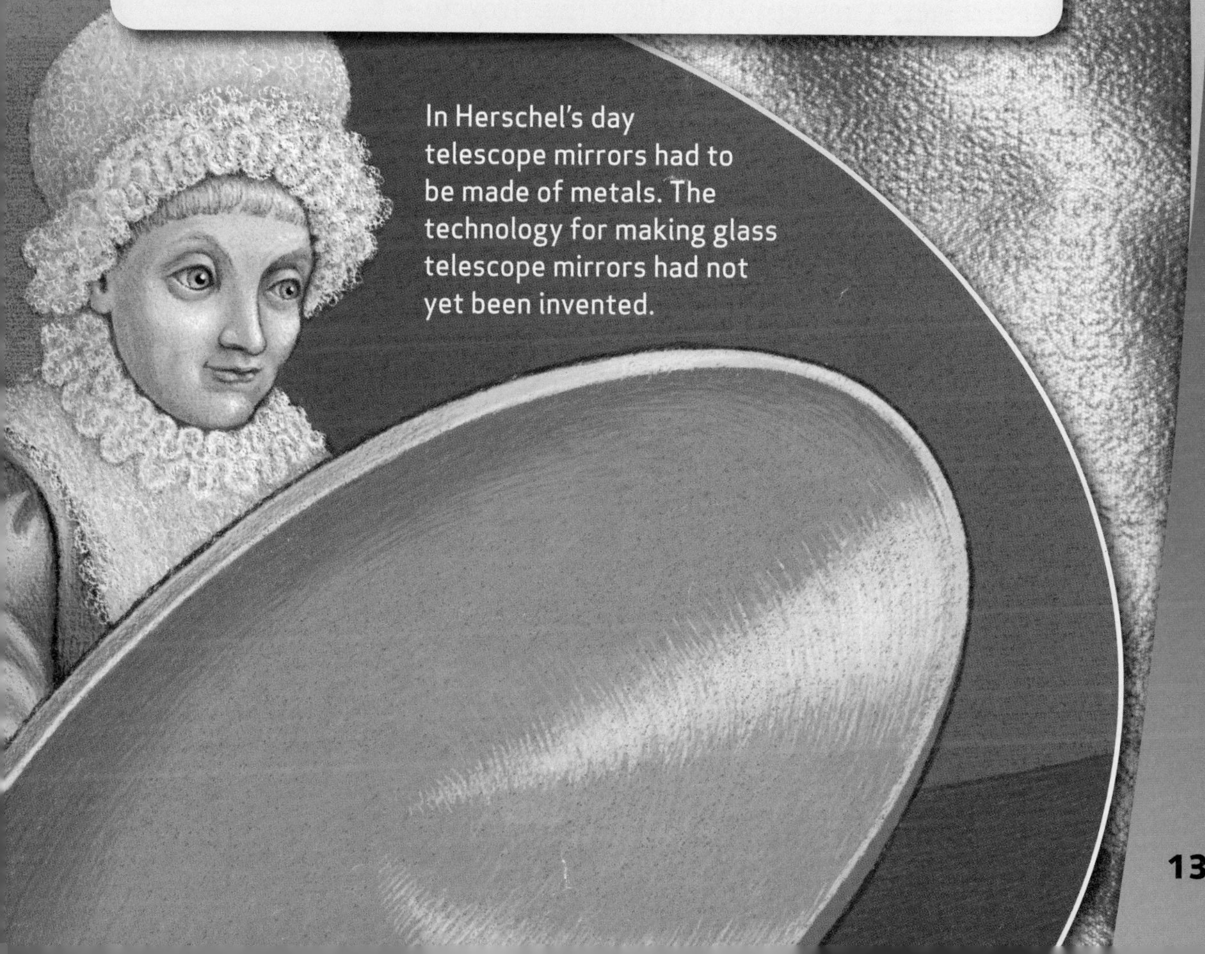

In Herschel's day telescope mirrors had to be made of metals. The technology for making glass telescope mirrors had not yet been invented.

Discovering a Planet

Using his own telescope, Herschel made **surveys** of the objects in the sky. Caroline and their brother, Alexander, helped him. Herschel noticed an unusual, or strange, object during a third survey of the sky in 1781. It was shaped a little like a disk, or round and flat. He watched it for months. He thought it might be a comet. But his math work showed that it moved in circles. Large objects that **revolve** like this around the sun are planets. Their circle-shaped paths are called orbits.

Herschel realized what that meant. He had discovered a planet! News of what he found spread fast. Suddenly he was famous. He was the first person in recorded history to discover a planet.

Some astronomers wanted to name the new planet Herschel, after its discoverer. Herschel wanted to name it after the King of England, George III. But most scientists wanted to name it after an ancient god like the other planets. They named it Uranus, for the Greek god of the heavens and father of Saturn.

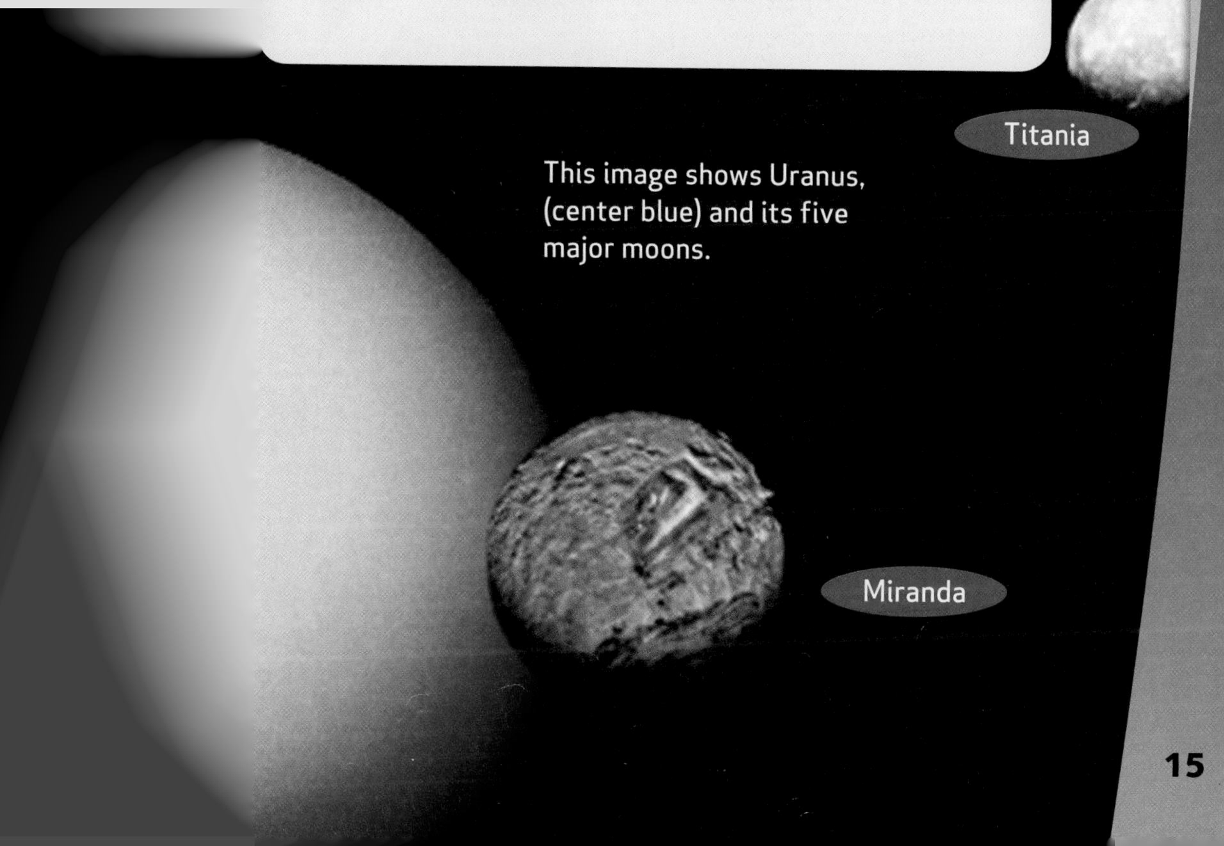

Titania

This image shows Uranus, (center blue) and its five major moons.

Miranda

A New Life for Herschel

Herschel's discovery changed his life. The Royal Society of London awarded him a medal. He became greatly respected by the scientific community.

In 1782 Herschel became the Royal Astronomer. He began to receive money each year from the king. He could now **devote** his whole life to studying the skies. He and Caroline moved near Windsor Castle, the home of the king. Caroline began "comet hunting" with her own telescope.

Herschel built this telescope for his sister, Caroline.

Wandering Planets

Mercury, Venus, Mars, Jupiter, and Saturn were known in ancient times. That's because they could be easily seen from Earth with the eye alone. As these planets circled the sun, they appeared to wander in the night sky. In fact, the word planets comes from the Greek word *planetes*, meaning "wanderer." Until Uranus and Neptune were discovered, most people believed these five planets were the only planets in the sky. They are all less than 750 million miles from Earth. But Uranus and Neptune are too far to see clearly without a telescope. They are both more than 1.5 billion miles away.

Source: NASA

How Herschel Watched the Night Sky

Telescopes made today are more **complicated** than ones made in the past. Today's telescopes can aim at an object and, without needing a person's help, follow it for a certain length of time as it moves in the sky. But Herschel had to move his telescope himself or have someone help him. Only one small area in the sky could be seen at once. He would aim for one point and observe what came through his field of view. Then he would move it to the next point. In order to look through the scope, he stood on a ladder.

Herschel made observations from the platform of this 20-foot telescope, while an assistant used the levers at the bottom to move the telescope.

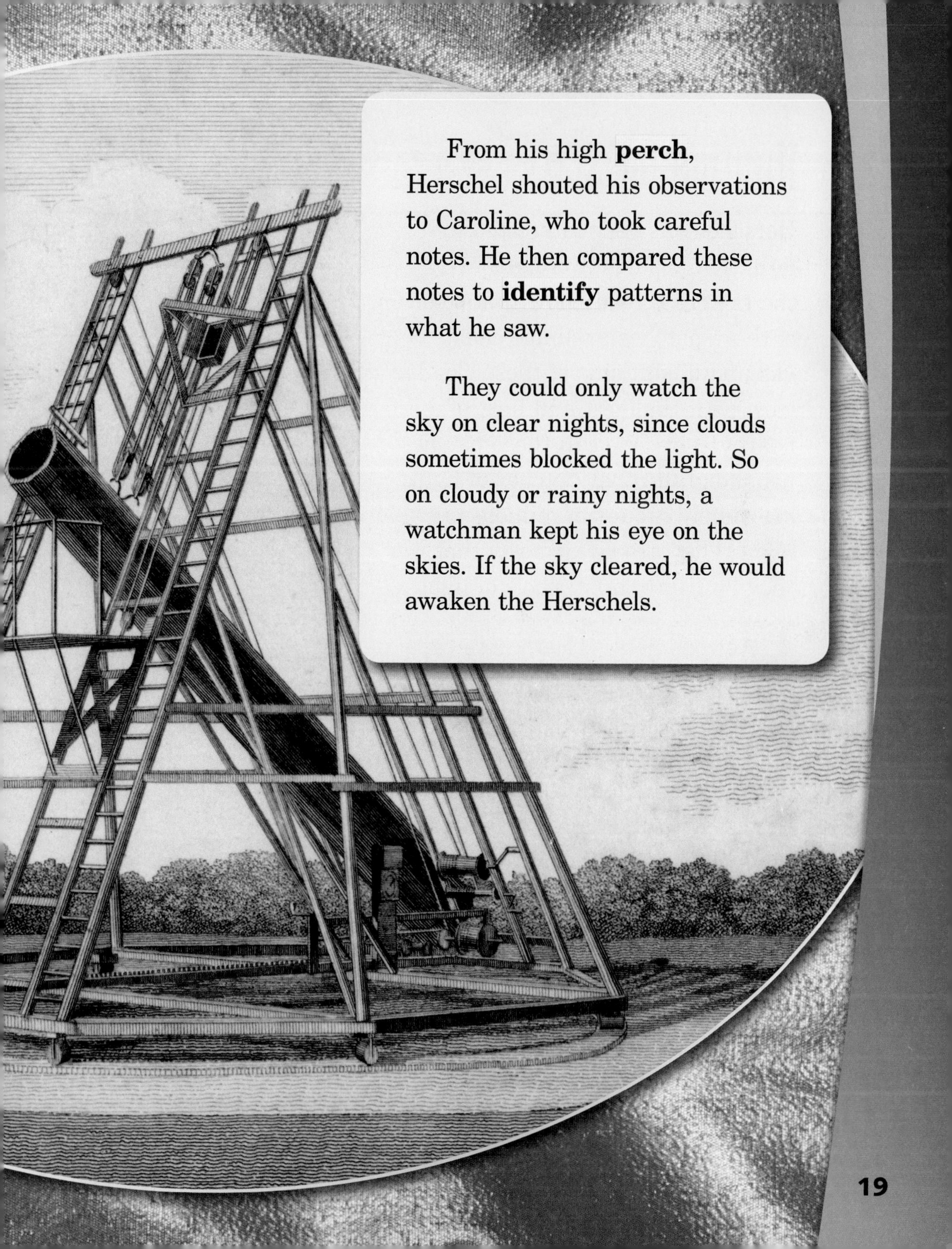

From his high **perch**, Herschel shouted his observations to Caroline, who took careful notes. He then compared these notes to **identify** patterns in what he saw.

They could only watch the sky on clear nights, since clouds sometimes blocked the light. So on cloudy or rainy nights, a watchman kept his eye on the skies. If the sky cleared, he would awaken the Herschels.

Hunting for Stars

Herschel was very interested in faint, fuzzy patches of light in the sky. Today we know that some of these patches are huge clouds of gas and dust. Some of these clouds glow with the light and heat of nearby stars. We call these patches nebulae. But other patches of light are simply groups of millions of stars. They are so far away that they blur into milky pools of light.

Astronomers in Herschel's time could not clearly see any of these patches, so they called all of them nebulae. Some astronomers thought nebulae were made of glowing fluid. Others wondered if they were groups of stars.

This is Orion's Nebula, one of the nebulae that Herschel studied. He first observed it in 1774.

Herschel directed his strongest telescope at some of the patches of light and saw groups of stars. He could not see stars in other patches, so he decided they were were simply too far away to focus on. He reasoned that his telescope wasn't strong enough to see the spaces between these distant stars. That would make them look like a single body of light.

Herschel and Caroline found more than 2,500 of these patches of light. Like other astronomers, they called them nebulae. But today we know that groups of stars are different from giant clouds of gas. Now astronomers only call the gas clouds nebulae. Many of these clouds will one day form stars.

Though Herschel was not right about all the nebulae, his observations and thoughtful arguments showed astronomers better ways to study the sky. Herschel's careful use of math to find patterns in the sky was a guide for astronomers everywhere.

Herschel believed that understanding the patterns in the night sky could help define the shape, size, and nature of our universe.

Herschel also attempted to explain how patterns in the sky related to time. He reasoned that **gravity** likely draws stars together over a long time, so stars that are bunched together must be old, and those that are spread out must be new. This wasn't true either, but it showed an important new way of thinking about space: some objects might be different because they were much older.

A Lifetime of Discoveries

In 1787 Herschel discovered two moons of Uranus: Titania and Oberon. Two years later he finished a telescope that was 40 feet long. He built it using money from King George III. Its mirror was four feet wide. It was also very, very heavy and hard to use. But it drew visitors from all over and allowed him to make another amazing discovery. Through this telescope, he found the sixth and seventh moons of Saturn: Enceladas and Mimas.

Herschel watched the patterns made by double stars, known as binary stars.

Herschel also looked at **binary** stars, or double stars. He closely tracked the pattern of their movements. By observing the way they moved, he discovered that they were not just close together. The two stars were both orbiting the same spot of empty space! Because of their gravity, the stars were pulling on each other. The spot they orbited was right between them. They were orbiting each other.

In 1789 Herschel completed work on the largest telescope of its time.

Drawing the Milky Way

Herschel was the first person to make a drawing of the Milky Way Galaxy that was nearly correct. He counted the stars in different regions of the sky and realized that the galaxy must be shaped like a disk. He thought our solar system sat in the center of the galaxy, though astronomers would later learn that it is much closer to the edge.

To honor his great career, the King of England made Herschel a knight in 1816. He will always be best known for his discovery of Uranus, but he made many important advances in the way we think about space. Though astronomers know today that Herschel was not right about everything, they also know that he did amazing work with the very few tools he had. His observations helped us to learn what we know now. Herschel even discovered a special part of light, called infrared light, that later allowed us to see our place in the Milky Way Galaxy. Long after the 1800s, Herschel's work is still helping us to bring the universe into focus.

Herschel's drawing of the Milky Way

While investigating heat using a prism and sunlight, Herschel also discovered infrared light.

Focus Question: What patterns and cycles do we find in space?

A Check Understanding

Make a list of the patterns and cycles William Herschel found while studying space. PRACTICE COMPANION 293

B Understand Text Features

Look at the bar graph on page 17. Show the bar graph to a partner. Explain what information in the text the graph helps you understand.

C Share and Compare

Compare your list of patterns and cycles with a partner's list. Are any of the patterns and cycles the same? Are any different? Explain why.

D Think Critically

Why do people study space? Use examples from the selection to explain.

Think Ahead
Selection 2

Focus Question: How did people of the past explain objects in the night sky?

Selection Connection

You have learned about the kinds of discoveries scientists have made about patterns and cycles in space. In the next selection you will learn why people study space.

Show What You Know

Think about the following: *the moon, the stars*, and *the sky at night*. Do you know any stories about these things? Write your ideas.

PRACTICE COMPANION 294

Preview

How did people of the past explain objects in the night sky? Preview pages 30–53. Then read *What's in Space?* to find out.

Selection 2

WHAT'S IN SPACE?

by Karen Baicker

CHAPTER 1 Our Solar System

People from the earliest of times gazed at the sky. They watched the sun, moon, and twinkling stars. They were amazed at how the moon looked different from one week to the next. They counted months by watching the **lunar** cycles. People also noticed five other objects in the sky. These were bigger than stars, but they did not twinkle. They were planets.

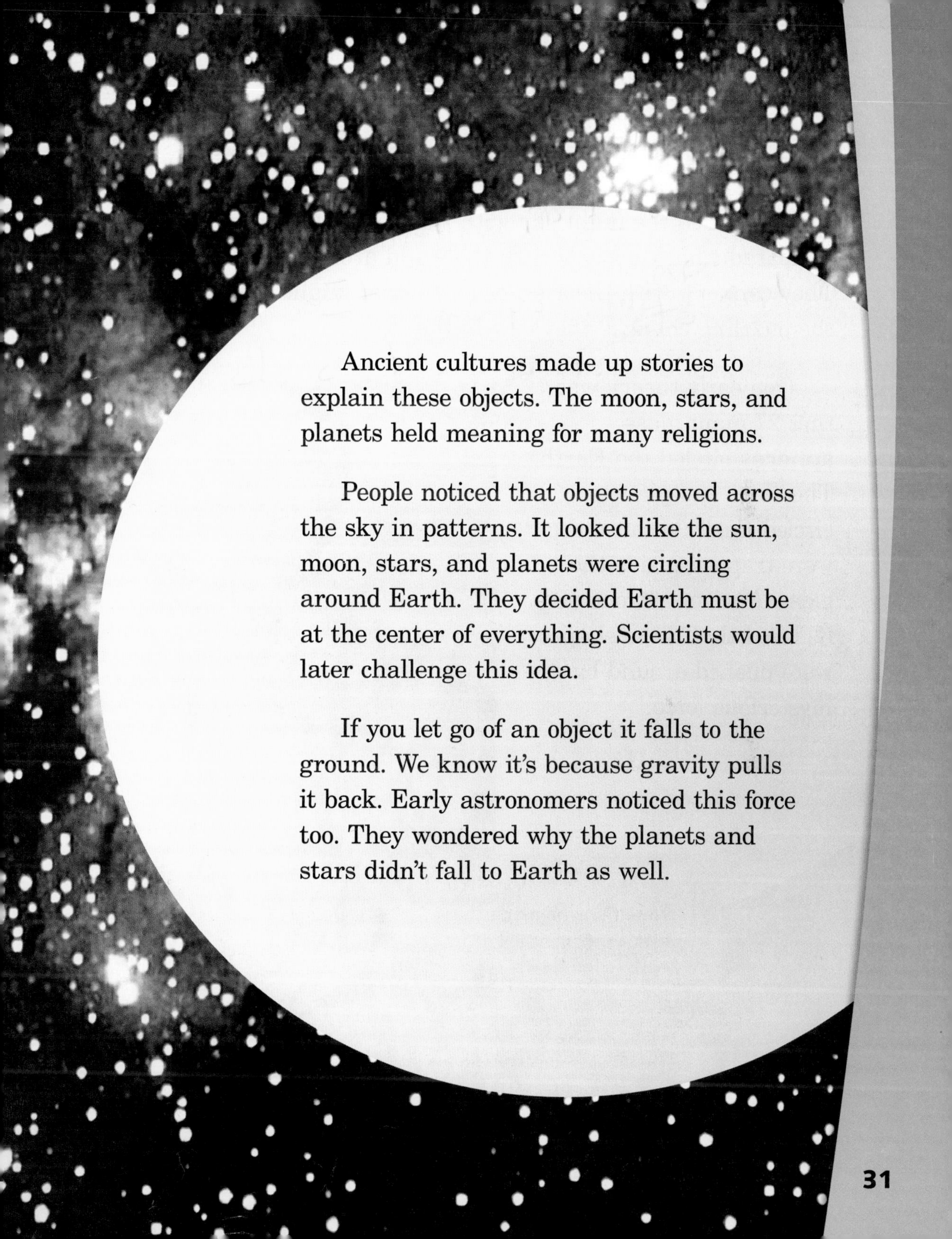

Ancient cultures made up stories to explain these objects. The moon, stars, and planets held meaning for many religions.

People noticed that objects moved across the sky in patterns. It looked like the sun, moon, stars, and planets were circling around Earth. They decided Earth must be at the center of everything. Scientists would later challenge this idea.

If you let go of an object it falls to the ground. We know it's because gravity pulls it back. Early astronomers noticed this force too. They wondered why the planets and stars didn't fall to Earth as well.

Ancient astronomers did not have the same tools we use today. There were no telescopes or satellites. Instead people studied the night sky with their eyes. They compared what they saw with the world around them. They came up with theories, or ideas, that might explain the puzzling changes they saw in the sky.

One early theory was that 27 giant glass **spheres** circled the Earth. The stars and planets circled Earth because they were trapped inside the glass. Ancient astronomers believed that these shapes were pushed around by a mysterious force.

Eudoxus was a Greek astronomer who made the first advanced model of the solar system.

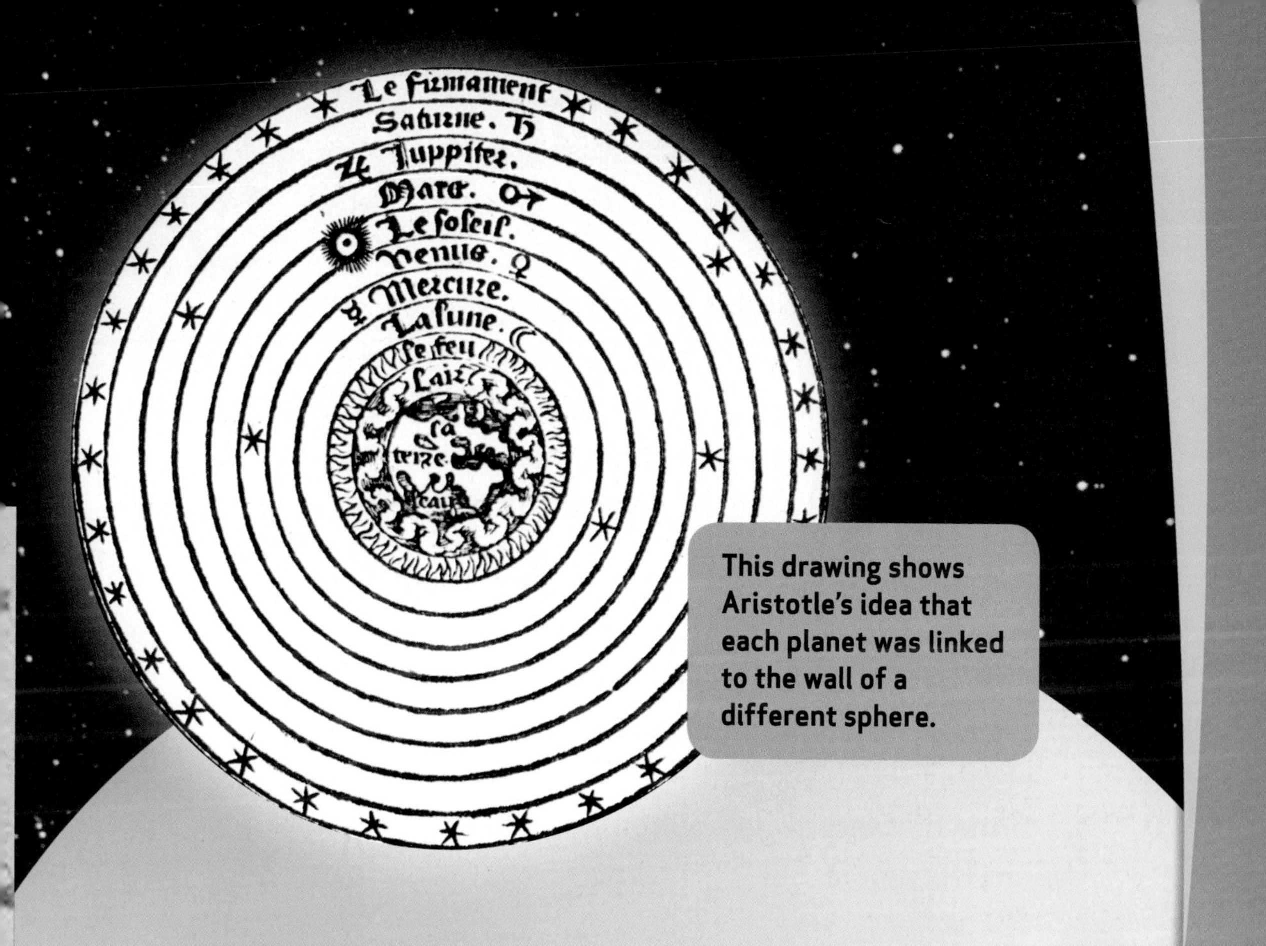

This drawing shows Aristotle's idea that each planet was linked to the wall of a different sphere.

About 2,300 years ago, Greek **philosophers** such as Plato and Aristotle came up with more detailed theories. Aristotle used math to draw a series of 56 spheres, one inside the other. He thought they carried the planets around Earth. Most people believed this explanation for over a thousand years.

The word *astronomy* comes from the Greek words *astron,* meaning "star," and *nomos,* meaning "law and order." The ancient Greeks were trying to figure out the law and order of the universe.

CHAPTER 2 Scientific Discoveries

In the early 1600s the telescope was invented. It helped people get a closer view of faraway objects. A scientist in Italy named Galileo made a telescope for himself. He made some improvements to it and then turned it toward the night sky.

He was able to see things he could not see **previously**. Galileo discovered that the moon had craters on it. He saw sunspots on the sun. He noticed that Jupiter had tiny spots of light circling it. These light spots were not always the same distance from Jupiter. Sometimes they could not be seen at all.

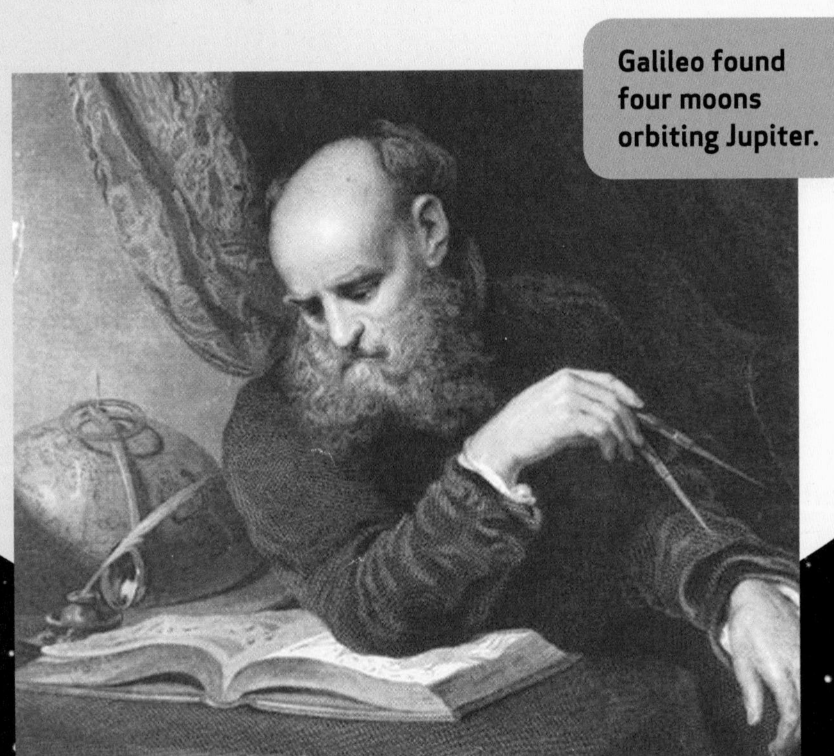

Galileo found four moons orbiting Jupiter.

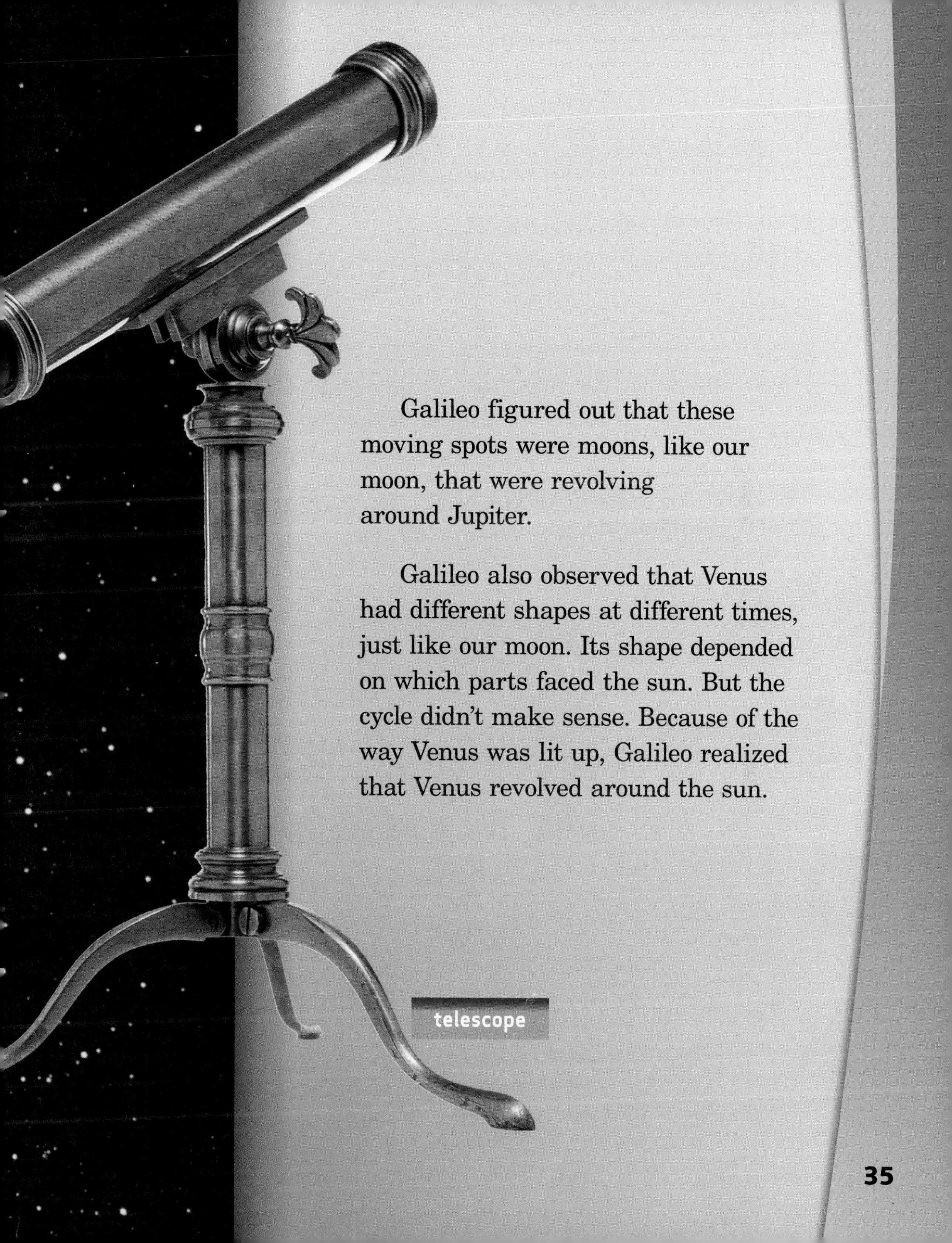

Galileo figured out that these moving spots were moons, like our moon, that were revolving around Jupiter.

Galileo also observed that Venus had different shapes at different times, just like our moon. Its shape depended on which parts faced the sun. But the cycle didn't make sense. Because of the way Venus was lit up, Galileo realized that Venus revolved around the sun.

Galileo's ideas were startling at the time. Perhaps Earth was not the center of the universe after all. If Jupiter and Venus circled the sun, while moons circled around Jupiter, what other possibilities were there? Perhaps Earth circled the sun, while the moon circled Earth.

Other astronomers used telescopes to eventually answer these questions. The more they could see of the night sky, the more they **craved** information about the rest of the universe. Still, it took hundreds of years for most people to accept the idea that the planets move around the sun, not around Earth.

Telescopes helped people discover some of Saturn's 53 moons. New moons are still being found.

Newton's Laws

A seventeenth century scientist named Isaac Newton had some important ideas about space. It had been discovered by another scientist that the planets do not move in a circle, but in an **ellipse**. Newton came up with theories about how and why the planets moved. He figured out that the laws of gravity existed not only on Earth, but also on the other planets.

Isaac Newton

CHAPTER 3 Learning about Earth

By the 1700s the sun, Earth, and other planets and their moons were known as the solar system. The word *solar* means "of the sun." A solar system describes the sun as the center of the system of planets. But even when people knew this to be true, there were still many **inaccurate** ideas about the planets.

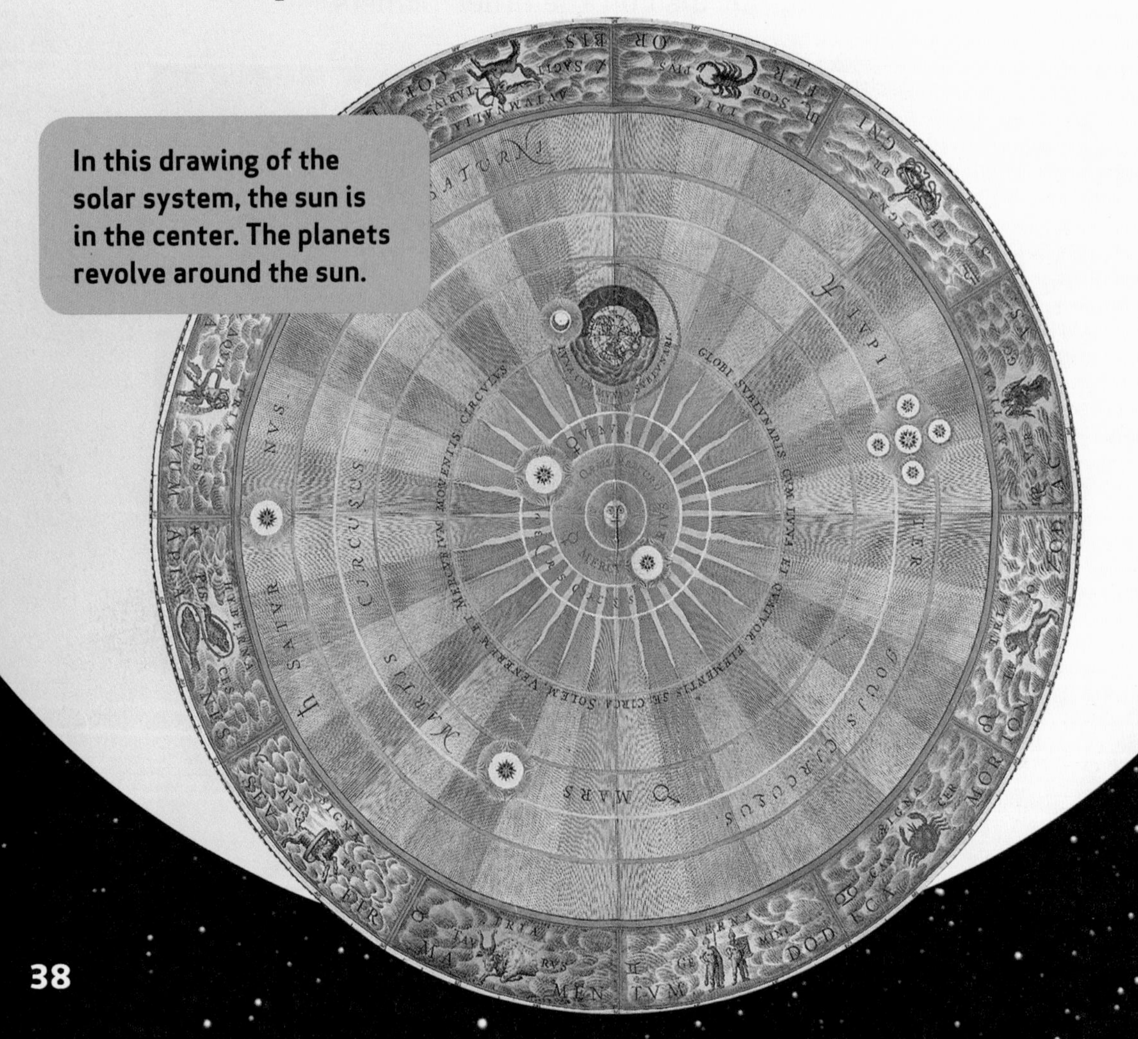

In this drawing of the solar system, the sun is in the center. The planets revolve around the sun.

If you stand and look out at the horizon, Earth appears flat.

Thousands of years ago, people thought Earth was flat. They could not see the curve of Earth with their eyes. But in the fourth century BC, Aristotle observed that there were stars that could be seen in one place but not in another. This could only happen on a curved surface. Aristotle believed that Earth was round, like a sphere.

Later, in the sixteenth century, explorers set out on trips at sea that proved Earth was a sphere. In the seventeenth century Galileo was able to tell that other planets in the solar system were spheres as well by using his newly invented telescopes. But none of this evidence let people see with their own eyes that the Earth was round.

By the twentieth century, however, science and technology had advanced. Scientists used satellites to take pictures of Earth's horizon. These pictures showed the curve of Earth. People were finally able to see with their own eyes that Earth was round.

Our theories about objects in the sky have changed over the centuries. As science and technology advance, so does our understanding of Earth and the solar system. The more advanced the instruments, the more detailed the information we can gather.

This photo shows what Earth looks like from space. You can see the curve of the planet.

Consider what we've learned about Earth's speed. Instruments in space tell us that the sun is around 93 million miles from Earth. That means Earth travels about 584 million miles to circle the sun each year. It moves 18.5 miles every second!

We have also learned more about how objects in space relate to each other. Light measurements tell us that some of the sun burns away over time. As the sun loses matter, its gravity becomes weaker. Its pull on Earth is not as strong. Our planet has slipped a tiny bit farther away from the sun than where it was a million years ago.

CHAPTER 4 Learning about Mars

Long ago, when people stared at the night sky, one planet stood out in particular. It glowed red. The Romans named the planet Mars, after the god of war. They did so because red is the color of blood. If you walked on the surface of Mars, you would see that it actually has a yellowish-brown color. This is caused by the large amounts of iron in its soil.

Mars has two moons. They each have dark names. One moon is named Phobos, which means "fear" in Greek. The other is named Deimos, which means "terror" in Greek.

For many years people wondered if there was life on Mars. Of all the planets, Mars seemed to be the most like Earth. One scientist studied Mars closely for years. He saw long, dark lines crossing the planet. He called these lines "channels." People thought he meant "canals." They took this to mean that some life form had built canals to carry water. Some thought there must be life on Mars!

Astronomers drew maps of what they saw through their telescopes. This drawing, made in 1877, maps some of the channels on Mars.

Many people have imagined that there is life on Mars. But no life forms have been found.

Many people have spent years trying to prove there is life on Mars. Scientists have found signs that there was once water on the planet. Some of the land looks like water once carved a path across it. Water is needed to support life. So some believe life on Mars was possible. But scientists have found no signs of life as we know it on the planet.

In 2004 this robot landed on Mars to study the planet for signs that water once covered the surface.

With powerful telescopes and space exploration, scientists continue to study Mars. What they have found does not give much hope for discovering life on Mars. The strong sunlight would harm most life forms, and the nights are very cold. Temperatures can drop to 220° F below zero. Giant dust storms are common on Mars too. Sometimes they swallow the planet for days. It is difficult to imagine lifeforms surviving such conditions.

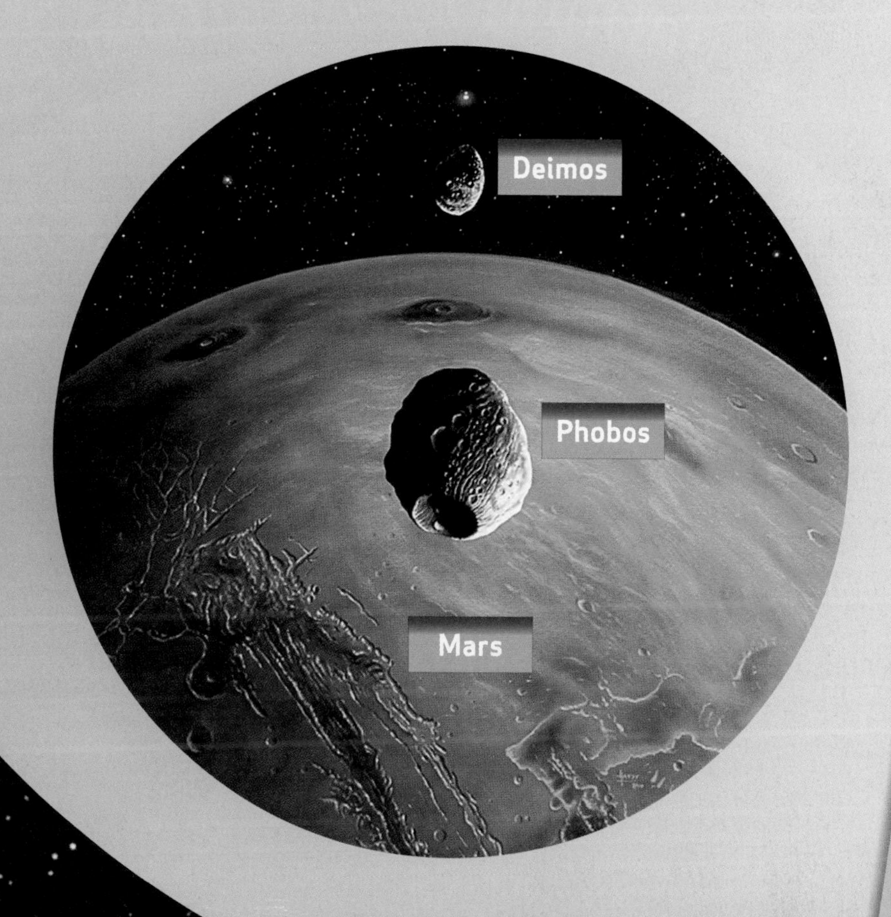

CHAPTER 5 Learning About Other Planets

Before the days of telescopes, people believed there were only five planets. That's all they could see. Then they discovered the outer planets. For many years after that, people were taught that the solar system had nine planets. Students remembered their names using this saying: "**M**y **V**ery **E**ducated **M**other **J**ust **S**erved **U**s **N**ine **P**izzas." The first letter in each word stood for the first letter of each planet in the order of their distance from the sun: Mercury, Venus, Earth, Mars, Jupiter, Saturn, Uranus, Neptune, Pluto.

This drawing shows what scientists think the surface of Pluto looks like. You can see Charon, Pluto's largest moon, in the sky.

Now that trick no longer works. That's because in 2006 scientists decided that Pluto is not actually a planet. Scientists discovered more and more objects in space. They had to decide what was a planet and what was not. One of the **factors** was size. Pluto did not make the cut. It is too small. Now it is known as a dwarf planet. So, for now, the solar system has eight planets. (Try: **M**y **V**ery **E**ducated **M**other **J**ust **S**erved **U**s **N**achos!)

The graph below shows approximately how long it takes the planets and a few other objects to make a full revolution around the sun. You can also see how long it takes them to complete a rotation and how fast they travel on average.

	Revolution	Rotation	Speed of orbit (miles per second)
Mercury	88 Earth days	59 Earth days	30
Venus	225 days	243 days	22
Earth	1 year	24 hours	19
Mars	687 days	25 hours	15
Saturn	29 years	11 hours	6
Jupiter	12 years	10 hours	8
Uranus	84 years	17 hours	4
Neptune	165 years	16 hours	3
Ceres (dwarf planet)	5 years	9 hours	11
Pluto (dwarf planet)	248 years	6 Earth days	3
Halley's Comet	76 years	52 hours	43 (when near Earth)

Sources: NASA, University Corporation for Atmospheric Research, Encarta, Astronomical Observatory of Pavoda

Neptune

Venus

Jupiter

Sun

Uranus

Mars

Mercury

Earth

Saturn

The orbit lines in this image help you understand each planet's distance from the sun.

It seems that information about the planets is changing every day. Scientists are always discovering new moons and learning new facts about our neighbors in space. Facts can quickly become outdated as we explore the planets with new technologies. Here are some facts that scientists today know about the planets.

Planet Extremes	
Largest Planet	Jupiter
Smallest Planet	Mercury
Coldest Planet	Neptune
Hottest Planet	Venus
Fastest Orbit	Mercury
Strongest Winds	Neptune

Earth is not the only planet with volcanoes. Olympus Mons is located on Mars. It is the largest volcano in the solar system.

Planet Facts

	Diameter *(in miles)*	Distance from sun *(in miles)*	Fact
Mercury	3,032	35,983,095	If you stood on Mercury, the sun would appear about 3 times larger than seen from Earth.
Venus	7,520	67,237,910	Venus is the second-brightest object in the night sky and is sometimes called the Morning or Evening Star.
Earth	7,926	92,955,820	Earth is the only planet known to have life.
Mars	4,222	141,633,260	Mars has the deepest canyon of all the planets.
Jupiter	88,846	483,682,810	Jupiter is not solid. It is mostly made of gas and has at least 62 moons.
Saturn	74,898	885,904,700	Saturn has "rings" made of chunks of ice and rock.
Uranus	31,763	1,783,939,400	Uranus is the only planet that spins sideways.
Neptune	30,778	2,795,084,800	Neptune has the slowest orbit. Since its discovery over 160 years ago, it has not completed one trip around the sun.

Beyond the Solar System

Earth is just one planet in our huge solar system. But the solar system is just a tiny part of a far bigger part of space: our galaxy. Our galaxy is called the Milky Way. The Milky Way Galaxy holds at least 100 billion stars. On a clear, dark night, you can see the Milky Way as a band of stars in space.

The sun seems so bright to us because it is the closest star in our solar system. People have wondered if any of the other stars in the universe are circled by planets. Scientists thought they might, but until recently they had no **proof**.

In 1991, scientists found some planets circling a star far outside our solar system. Since then, scientists have found more than 330 other planets. There are at least 280 stars with their own planets circling them.

Scientists keep looking farther and farther into space. There will always be more discoveries offering the hope of life beyond Earth. Scientists are planning to send spacecraft beyond our solar system. Who knows what the future will bring?

This photo shows the Milky Way Galaxy. It takes 100,000 years for light to travel from one end to the other.

Focus Question: How did people of the past explain objects in the night sky?

A Check Understanding

How did people of the past explain the planets in the night sky? How do their ideas differ from what we know now? PRACTICE COMPANION 310

B Understand Text Features

An index is an alphabetical list of subjects found at the back of the book. Page numbers help you find the subjects within the book. Using the index, where would you find information about Mars? Share your information with a partner.

C Share and Compare

Make a list of past ideas about objects in space. Compare your list with a partner's list. Which ideas are the same? Which are different? Why?

D Think Critically

Why do people study space? Use examples from the selection to explain.

Think Ahead
Selection 3

Focus Question: How do people view space today?

Selection Connection

You have learned how people of the past were inspired by the night sky. In the next selection you will learn why people study space.

Show What You Know

Think about the following: *telescopes*, *satellites*, and *space vehicles*. How do these things help us view space? Write your ideas.

PRACTICE COMPANION 311

Preview

How do people view space today?
Preview pages 56–77. Then read *Living in Space* to find out.

Selection 3

LIVING IN SPACE

by Dina McClellan

Illustrated by Zues Bacon

Chapter 1
My Daughter, the Astronomer

"Need help carrying your telescope, Veronica? I can drive you, if that's easier."

"That's okay, Dad. It's not too heavy."

"The telescope is terrific," said Veronica's mother, touching her daughter's hair. "My little astronomer."

"*Our* little astronomer," Veronica's father said, patting his daughter on the back.

"You're acting like I won the contest already!" Veronica said. She knew how lucky she was to have supportive parents, but she often felt that their confidence in her was **undeserved**. She knew that out there in the real world, people would judge her on her worth—not because she was someone's "little astronomer."

"Anyway, the contest isn't until next week," Veronica reminded them. "I'm just bringing my telescope to school to show to Ms. Beale, in case she has any suggestions."

"How could she?" said Veronica's father. "It's perfect."

Her mother nodded enthusiastically. "Just think—our Veronica invented a telescope!"

"I didn't *invent* it, Mom. I just copied it from a book. It was invented a long time ago."

"Well, I know you'll make us proud," said Veronica's father. "And Grandma Flores will be so pleased to have an astronomer in the family again!"

Veronica kissed her parents goodbye and somehow got her science project out the door.

Grandpa Flores wasn't a real astronomer; he just loved looking at the sky. Veronica remembered the "spacewalks" they used to take together in the woods behind his house during one of the family's yearly visits to Argentina. Veronica was six when her grandfather died.

It was from Grandpa Flores that Veronica learned to love the night sky. As a four-year-old, Veronica looked at every star **formation** Grandpa Flores showed her; at five she knew about light-years, supernovas, black holes, and telescopes powerful enough to reach other galaxies. Grandpa Flores taught her how the universe is expanding, or growing.

Grandpa Flores knew a lot because he was curious about everything. He loved to take things apart and put them back together to see how they worked. People in his village would bring him their broken toasters, clocks—even their DVD players—and he'd carefully open them up and fix them.

When Veronica and her family would come to visit, they would spend hours in his cellar building models of rockets, spaceships, and even space stations. At night, she and Grandpa Flores would watch stars on the hills outside. The dark hills rose for miles, like huge waves in a rolling ocean of grass. Some nights were so clear that breaths of fog between the hills glowed white under the brilliant moon.

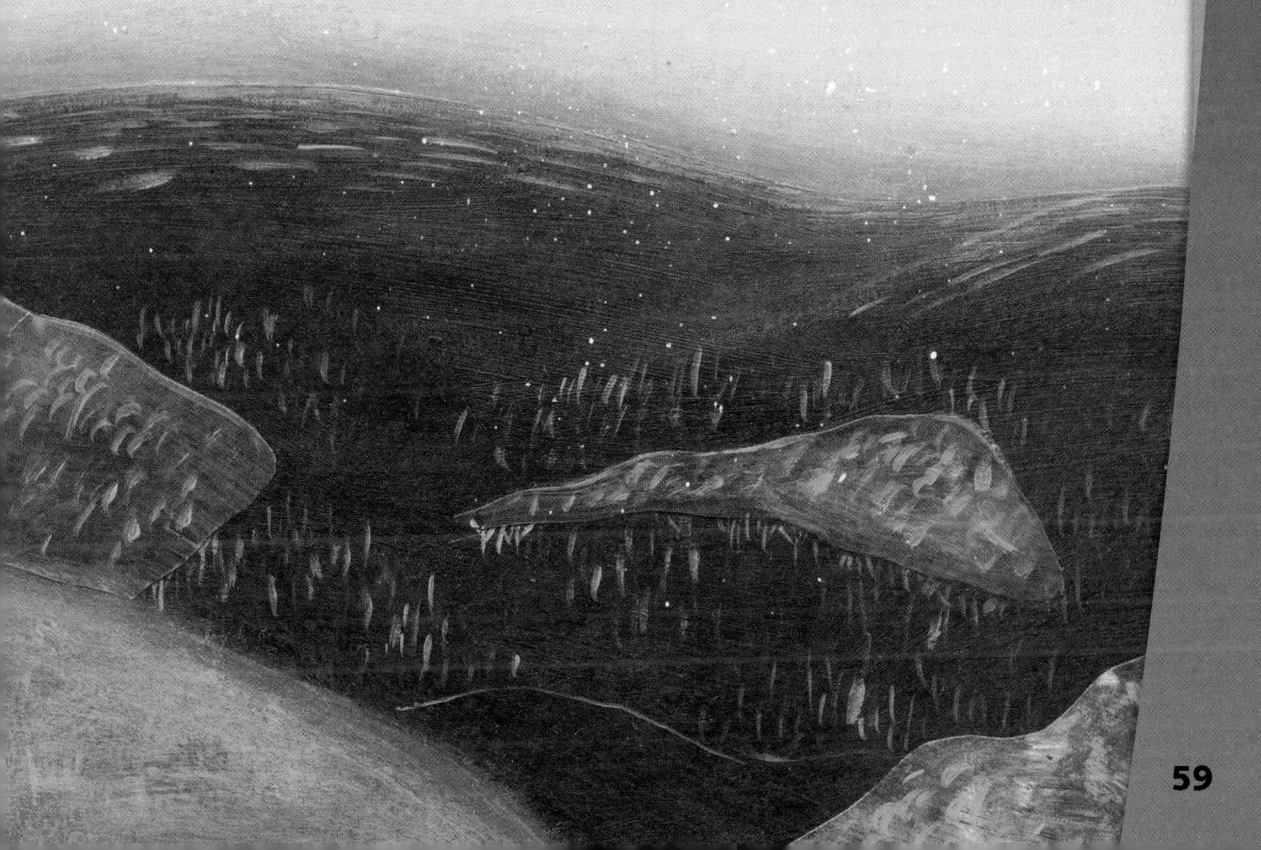

Veronica shared Grandpa Flores's curiosity and the way he loved to figure things out. No problem was ever too difficult for him to **tackle**. No question was too silly to be explored. When Grandpa Flores explained something, he made it easy to understand.

When Veronica wanted to know how long it would take a car to drive to Betelgeuse—a faraway star hundreds of light-years away from Earth—Grandpa Flores explained about light-years. He said that a light-year was the distance light can travel in one year. If you wrote out that distance in miles, the number would be close to a 6 followed by 12 zeros.

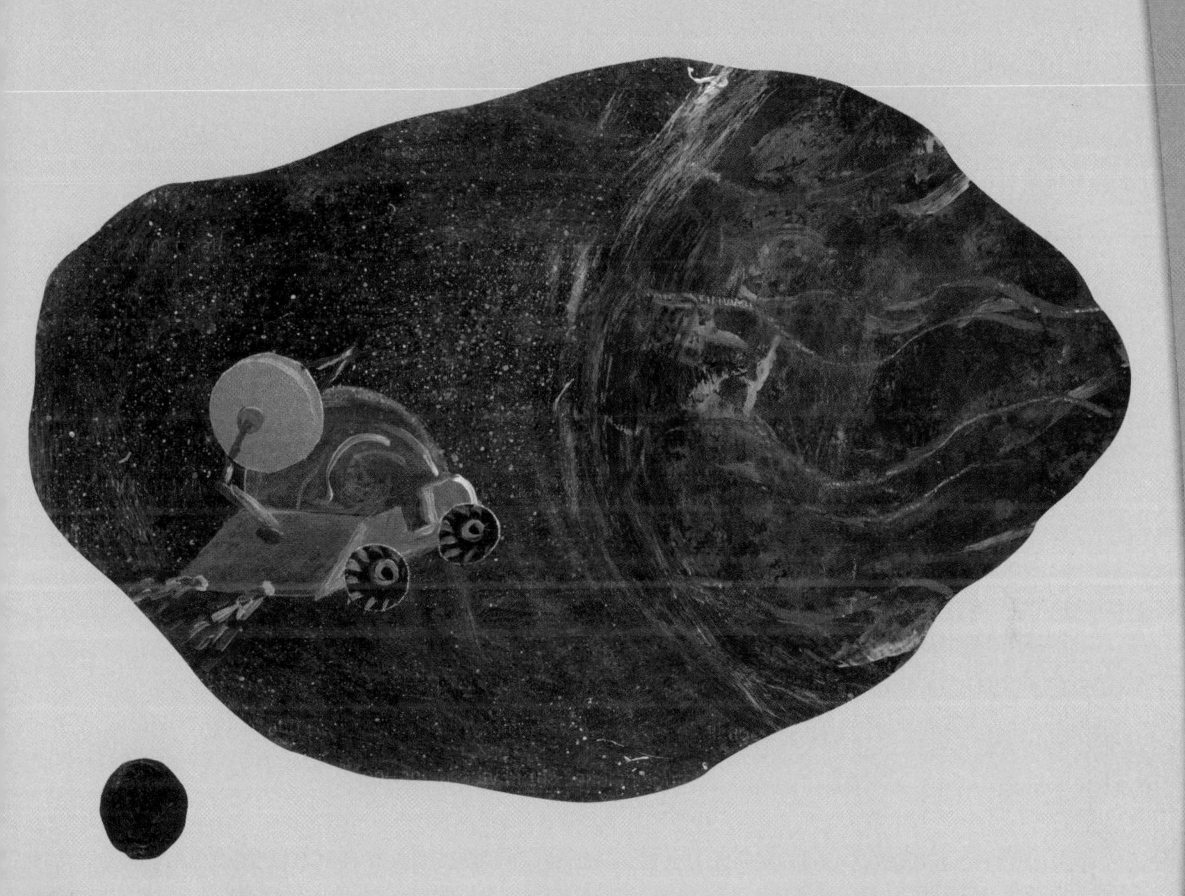

When Veronica asked if she could see Betelgeuse through a really powerful telescope, Grandpa Flores explained how light travels. He said that even if she *could* see Betelgeuse through a really powerful telescope, she'd be seeing it as it *used* to be, not as it was now.

"That's because the light from Betelgeuse takes so long to travel to Earth," he explained.

Veronica was impressed. She wondered if it worked the other way: *What would people on Betelgeuse see if they aimed telescopes toward Earth? Would they see medieval knights?*

Chapter 2 Crashing

Now, five years later, Veronica found herself returning to that earlier talk.

What would Grandpa Flores think of her now? she wondered. *What would he say if he knew his granddaughter was on the* **verge** *of winning an important science competition? How proud would he be?*

He would have been just as proud as he had been when she asked all those dumb questions as a young child, Veronica realized. Grandpa Flores would have been proud of her no matter what.

Veronica was very deep in thought. She didn't notice the group of kids charging into school, but she did feel a sudden

jolt as someone ran into her telescope, and she heard a sharp crack as it fell to the sidewalk. It had broken into several pieces. Even the expensive glass lenses were shattered.

"Sorry!" a younger kid yelled out, still running toward the school. He thought he'd only brushed her arm.

Then everything went blank. Veronica had a heavy, sinking feeling of disaster. Her arms and legs felt like blocks of stone. With her **magnificent** telescope in pieces, she'd never win the competition. She would never impress Ms. Beale, or make her parents proud, or go to space camp, or be an astronaut . . .

Somehow Veronica collected the pieces of her broken project. She dumped them in the garbage. Ms. Beale tried to **console** her. She gave Veronica an extension. But Veronica couldn't help thinking about all the people she was letting down.

After school Veronica went straight home. She felt too **miserable** to hang out with the other kids. She went right to her room. She flung herself on her bed. A folded copy of *Life in Space* lay on the pillow where she'd left it. *Life in Space* was a magazine about life on the International Space Station.

Veronica wished she could live on the International Space Station. It would be a whole different world—or no world at all! Billions of miles of empty space would frame the stars, the moon, and beautiful, blue Earth in the distance. She would float through the station's small rooms entirely weightless. Her telescope wouldn't fall and break in space! All her problems would wait back on Earth, while she worked and studied with astronauts from all over the planet. She wouldn't need to win a contest, either. She would already be a real astronaut.

Chapter 3
Other Earths

The magazine on Veronica's pillow was open to a story about life outside of Earth. The title was "Are We Alone?" Just that morning she'd been reading about the idea that life began on Mars billions of years ago when the planet was warm and wet. The surface of Mars now was too cold and dry to support life. But some scientists thought that simple life, such as bacteria, might still live deep under the surface of Mars. The story described how NASA sent a rover to search for Martian life.

Her thoughts began to drift. She guessed she could build the telescope again, with the extension. But then she thought of all the work she'd put in and she knew it wouldn't be the same.

She was **browsing** through the magazine when this bit of information caught her eye:

Scientists have discovered well over 300 planets of various sizes. However, most of these planets are bigger than Jupiter. Recently scientists found a small, Earth-like planet going around a star in our galaxy. They expect to find even more of these amazing discoveries.

Veronica's eyes began to close. She was so tired. But she was also interested in what she was reading, so she read on:

Scientists looked through powerful telescopes at a nearby star. They noticed that the star was sometimes less bright, and that it wobbled a tiny bit. They realized that a planet was orbiting the star. It blocked some of the light. Its gravity made the star appear to wobble. Scientists think the conditions on this planet may be close enough to Earth's that it could support life.

Is our solar system so special? Veronica thought. *Could there really be life on other planets?*

Questions ran through Veronica's head. *Is that part of the work they do on the International Space Station?* she wondered. *Are the astronauts up there gathering information on planets that can support life? Are scientists building a supertelescope powerful enough to see planets that are not even part of our solar system?*

Just then there was a knock on her bedroom door. Veronica thought it might be her mom wanting to know why she was in her room for so long. Or it could be her dad telling her to wash up for dinner.

Chapter 4
Top Secret

But the voice on the other side of the door belonged to neither her mom nor her dad. It was a woman's voice, the voice of a stranger.

"Veronica Flores?"

"Yes?"

"I'm Vicky Lee. I'd like to talk to you. May I come in?"

Veronica put down the magazine and opened the door. She was surprised to see a small dark-haired woman in an astronaut's suit standing in the doorway. Veronica guided her in and gave her a chair to sit on.

"You're an astronaut?" Veronica asked, eyes wide in disbelief.

"Yes," said the woman. "I work at the International Space Station. I've come here on official business. May I be direct?"

"Sure," said Veronica, although she wasn't sure about anything.

"You must promise not to breathe a word about this to anyone," said Vicky Lee.

"Not a word," Veronica said. This was beginning to sound interesting.

"I'm working on a project. I can only tell you that it's top secret and that it involves a highly sophisticated telescope," said Ms. Lee. "Have you ever heard of the James Webb Space Telescope?"

Veronica had. It used to be called the Next Generation Space Telescope. It is even more high-tech than the Hubble Space Telescope.

“Well, it’s *not* the James Webb Telescope I’m talking about. The one *I* work with makes the James Webb Telescope look like a toy. It is a hundred times more powerful than any other telescope and is able to look back in time at the universe’s first stars. It can also look for life on other planets. ”

“Wow! That’s amazing!” said Veronica. “But what’s the problem?

"It's broken," said Ms. Lee. "A piece of it tore off. No one knows how that happened, and now it doesn't work. Hundreds of tests have been run, but nothing shows up. We're very worried because launch time for the telescope is in one week. We think you are the person to fix it."

Veronica gulped.

"If you accept the mission," continued Ms. Lee, "you will be transported immediately to the International Space Station. You will stay until the telescope is fully repaired."

"What happens if I fail?" Veronica asked, feeling ill.

"Failure is not an **option**," said Ms. Lee.

What about school? What do I tell my parents? wondered Veronica.

"Your parents have approved of the mission," Ms. Lee explained, as if she could read Veronica's thoughts. "Let's go—there's a car waiting for us outside."

Veronica and Vicky Lee were taken to a launching pad on a Pacific island. It reminded Veronica of Argentina. From there they soared away from Earth in a space shuttle headed for the International Space Station's Control **Module**. The module was already in orbit more than 200 miles above Earth. Veronica shut her eyes as the engines roared and Earth shrank beneath them.

The station they reached was as big as the inside of a jumbo jet. "Now watch," said Ms. Lee. She took off her seat belt and rose to the ceiling. Veronica did the same. Soon both of them were walking upside down and laughing uncontrollably.

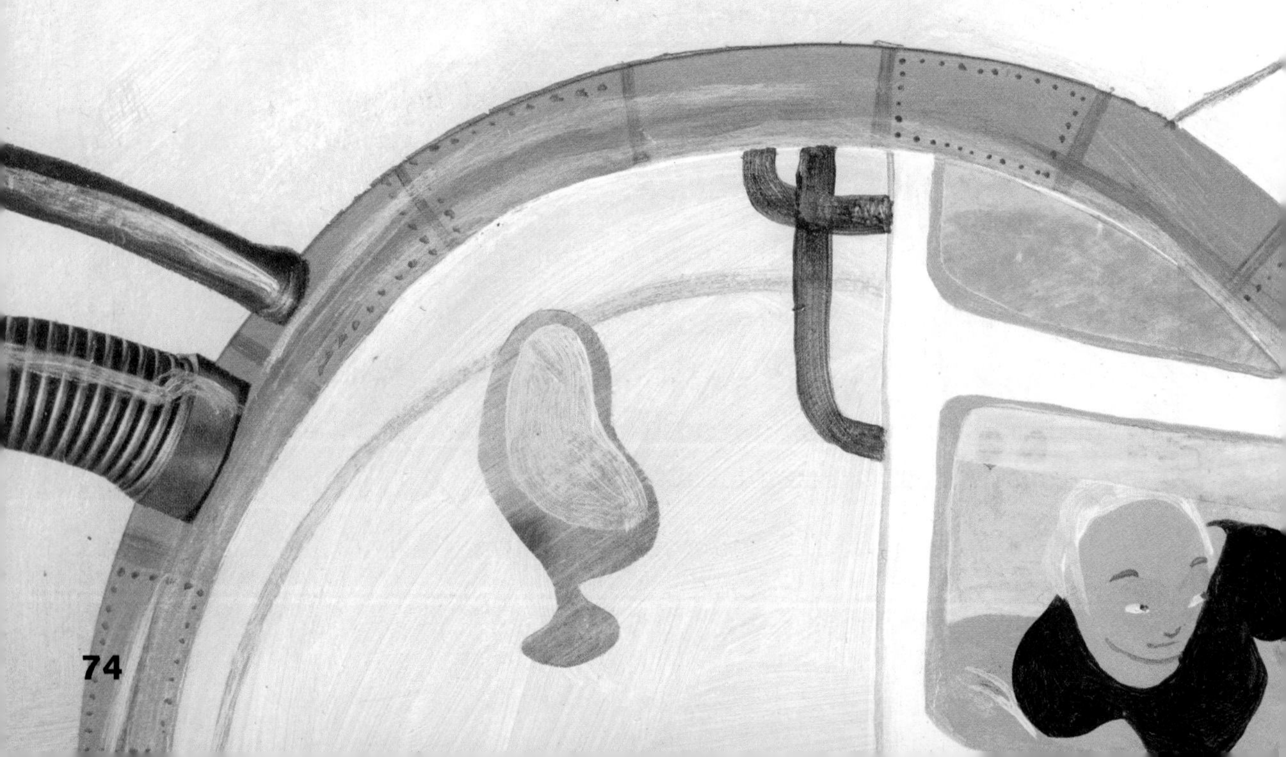

Later Ms. Lee took out tightly sealed containers of food and water for a snack. Then Ms. Lee showed her the new fitness wing. It had machines that let astronauts exercise in zero gravity.

"Time to get to work," said Ms. Lee suddenly. She floated up to a **slender** hall, which led to another hall. At the end of the second hall was the telescope. It was neatly cracked down the middle.

"I'll leave you to it," said Ms. Lee. "Don't lose focus!" she joked. "The future is in your hands, little astronomer."

Veronica looked at the broken telescope. One of its giant lenses had popped out and was floating around somewhere. Even so, the telescope was a thing of beauty. Veronica raised it and lowered it and turned it around on its base. She wanted to play with it. She wanted to take it apart and **marvel** at its many pieces. Suddenly she realized that even if it took days of work, fixing the telescope would be fun!

Suddenly a knock on the door made her jump five feet into the air.

Oh no—Vicky Lee! She had come back too soon, Veronica thought.

There was another knock. "Veronica! Are you coming down for dinner?"

Dinner? *Dinner*?

But it wasn't Vicky Lee—it was her mom calling to her!

Veronica tried to recall the dream, but could not. Even so, something inside her had changed. She felt lighter somehow, as if she were floating in zero gravity. It was the same feeling she'd had in Grandpa Flores's cellar, when she'd lose herself in a problem, when everything disappeared but the task at hand.

Veronica didn't know it yet, but she was about to start building another, better telescope.

Focus Question: How do people view space today?

A Check Understanding

Think about the different tools used for space exploration. How do these tools help us get a better view of space today? PRACTICE COMPANION 339

B Understand Literary Elements

Imagery is language that describes how someone or something looks, sounds, feels, smells, or tastes. Look for examples of imagery in your selection. Share your examples with a partner.

C Share and Compare

Make a list of space exploration tools discussed in your selection. Compare your list with a partner's list. Which tools are the same? Which tools are different? Why?

D Think Critically

Why do people study space? Use examples from the selection to explain.

Think Ahead
Selection 4

Focus Question: How might space be a part of our future?

Selection Connection

In *Living in Space* you have learned how people view space today. In the next selection you will learn what inspires people to study space.

Show What You Know

Think about the following: *space stations*; *minerals on other planets*; and *traveling to other planets*. How will these help space be a part of our future? Write your ideas.

PRACTICE COMPANION **340**

How might space be a part of our future? Preview pages 80–102. Then read *Dexter's Discovery* to find out.

Dexter's DISCOVERY

by Kathy Zahler • Illustrated by Colin Mier

Cast of Characters

DEXTER: a ten-year-old boy

RITA: Dexter's sister, age fifteen

MRS. REYNOLDS: Dexter and Rita's mother

MR. REYNOLDS: Dexter and Rita's father

DR. KANG: a scientist

ACT 1, SCENE 1: Dexter's home

*(*DEXTER *and his family live in a* ***compound*** *on Mars. The Reynolds' home is connected to other areas of the compound by a set of tunnels.)*

(It is early morning. DEXTER *is sitting at the kitchen table. He is surrounded by rocks. An empty box is at his feet. His sister* RITA *enters.)*

RITA: Dexter! Get those rocks off the table. Some of us would like to *eat* there!

DEXTER: In a minute. I'm just sorting through them quickly . . .

RITA: *(angrily)* Mom!

(MRS. REYNOLDS *enters, dressed in astronaut gear. She carries her helmet.*)

MRS. REYNOLDS: Kids, your father is trying to sleep. He worked late at the mine last night. Now Dexter, you know we had a deal. The rocks belong in your room, not in our shared living space.

DEXTER: Yes, Mom. I was just using the kitchen table because it's the biggest table we have. That way I can study more of my rocks side by side. I'll put them away. (*He begins to put each rock into its own place in the box.*)

MRS. REYNOLDS: (*Playfully ruffes his hair.*) Thank you, honey. Maybe I'll bring you a few more when I get home tonight. Rita, see that Dexter gets to school on time, please. I expect all homework to be done before I get back! (*She exits.*)

RITA: (*Shakes her head.*) Why don't you just play video games like the other kids? *(She pours herself a bowl of cereal and sits at the table.)*

DEXTER: I can play video games back on Earth. On Mars I want to learn about Mars. (*He holds up a rock.*) Did you know that this green stripe probably means that there was once water on Mars?

RITA: Honestly, Dexter—who cares? (*She puts her dishes in a dishwasher and exits.*)

DEXTER: Well, I care. If there was water, there might have been things living in that water. (*He runs his hand over the rocks. Suddenly he looks up at a clock on the wall.*) Oh, no! I'm late again! (*He exits, carrying the box.*)

ACT 1, SCENE 2: Dexter's home

(It is evening. DEXTER *sits at the kitchen table, viewing a rock with a magnifying glass. A second rock sits on the table next to him.* RITA *enters.)*

RITA: Are those new?

DEXTER: (*Holds up the rock.*) Mom brought them home from the mine.

RITA: She brought you *more* rocks to study? You must have half the mine in your room by now.

DEXTER: But some of these are special! Take a look. Isn't this one magnificent?

RITA: (*Rolls her eyes.*) Oh, yes. It's magnificent. Dexter, it looks just like all the others!

DEXTER: No, not really. This one has a funny mark along one side. You have to look carefully though. Can you see it? (*He tries to get* RITA *to look more closely, but she brushes him aside and both rocks fall to the ground.*) My rocks!

RITA: (*A little bit **ashamed.***) Sorry, Dexter. They're just rocks. They won't break.

DEXTER: (***Scrambles*** *under the table.*) Oh, no! They *did* break! One of them cracked right in two!

MR. REYNOLDS: (*Enters in astronaut gear.*) Hey, kids! What's all the noise?

RITA: I made Dexter drop his silly rocks, and one of them broke in two. (*She exits.*)

MR. REYNOLDS: Are you all right, sport? I heard a crash.

DEXTER: (*Gets up from under the table, rocks in hand.*) I'm okay. One of my rocks is broken. (*He sits and turns the rocks over and over.*)

MR. REYNOLDS: You know something, Dexter? I break rocks all day long in the mines. The rocks never **complain** about it. Why, just yesterday, we were working on a huge rock formation. One swing of the pick, and those rocks were all in pieces.

DEXTER: (*Looks pained.*) Yes, I know, Dad. Your job is to take rocks apart. My job is to collect them and study them.

MR. REYNOLDS: (*laughs*) Your job, hmmm? Well, it's good that you have a job to keep you busy. I think there are a few too *many* rocks at my job. Sometimes all I dream about is rocks. Big rocks, little rocks, falling rocks. All night! (*He puts on his helmet and exits.*)

DEXTER: (*to himself*) There's no such thing as too many rocks. (*He turns the rocks over and over. Then he picks up the magnifying glass and starts to study the broken rock. He holds the rock and the glass up to the light.*)

MRS. REYNOLDS: (*Enters in regular clothes.*) Is everything all right, Dexter? Rita told me that you were a little upset.

DEXTER: (*Stares through the magnifying glass at the broken rock.*) Umm, yes. No. I mean, everything is . . .

RITA: *(enters) Now* what are you doing? (*She and* MRS. REYNOLDS *begin to set the table for three.*) Dexter? (*She shakes her head.*) You see, Mom? He's just so weird sometimes. I wouldn't be surprised if I walked into the kitchen one day and found him talking to those rocks.

MRS. REYNOLDS: Now, Rita. (*to* DEXTER) What are you looking at, honey?

DEXTER: (*As if waking up suddenly.*) Huh? Oh! Mom, Rita—you won't believe this. Rita, it's so great that you made me drop those rocks!

MRS. REYNOLDS: What won't I believe? I don't know what you're talking about, Dexter! Slow down and tell me what happened.

DEXTER: (*Dances around, holding up both halves of the broken rock.*) Oh, Mom, this is the greatest discovery of all time! Take a look! (RITA *and* MRS. REYNOLDS *look closely at the rock halves.*) Look where I'm pointing. You can see it better with the magnifying glass.

MRS. REYNOLDS: Well . . . it looks a little bit like a leaf. It looks like a leaf of some kind was stuck in the rock.

RITA: (*Looks through the magnifying glass.*) Yes, it's definitely some kind of fossil left by a little plant. Through the magnifying glass you can see where all the tiny veins branch out from the stem. It looks like a regular leaf.

DEXTER: (*smiling*) Exactly! But doesn't something about that seem very unusual?

RITA: (*Catches on.*) Dexter! There are no leaves on Mars!

DEXTER: Right! Even our very best scientists have never found any proof that there was *ever* life on Mars.

MRS. REYNOLDS: *(Sits down suddenly.)* Goodness, children. Dexter, how can this be? I know exactly where I found the rock. It was part of the rock formation in the Delta Mine. We only opened that mine up yesterday morning. That was the first time anybody had ever went in there.

RITA: It is a fossil, I just know it! It's a fossil from Mars!

DEXTER: We need another opinion. We should take it to the Chief of Science, Dr. Kang. She will know what it means.

RITA: Wow, Dexter! (*She carefully wraps the rock halves in a napkin as* MRS. REYNOLDS *dials the phone.*)

ACT 2, SCENE 1: Dr. Kang's lab

(It is the next day. The Reynolds family is crowded into DR. KANG'S *bright white lab.* DEXTER *holds the rock halves.)*

MR. REYNOLDS: Well, Dr. Kang, I hate to waste your time . . .

DR. KANG: Not at all, not at all. I'm always happy to see you and your lovely family. So, Dexter, I hear that you made some sort of discovery.

DEXTER: (*shyly*) Well, Rita sort of helped.

DR. KANG: We haven't found anything new on Mars in quite a long time. What makes you so sure you've made a discovery?

MRS. REYNOLDS: Dexter, show Dr. Kang what you found.

DEXTER: (*Unwraps the rock halves.*) You may need a magnifying glass to see the **imprint**.

DR. KANG: (*Places the rock half under a viewer.*) Ah, yes, I see. It's a very nice fossil, children. It looks a bit like . . . well, not quite. (*She rubs her eyes and looks again.*) It's the sort of thing you find on the ocean floor near . . . but not exactly. (*She looks up.*) So you brought this from Earth? Where on Earth did you find it?

DEXTER: That's just it, Dr. Kang. It's not from Earth. The rock you're holding is from Mars.

DR. KANG: (*She shakes her head and looks through the viewer again.*) No, that's not right. The imprint looks a bit like . . . but it's not exactly . . .

MRS. REYNOLDS: It's true, though, Dr. Kang. I was in the Delta Mine. We had just opened **Zone** 3. As you know, that zone was closed until two days ago. I picked this rock up from a pile in that zone.

DR. KANG: It's just impossible. (*She stands up.*) Everyone knows very well that there are no plants on Mars. And we have never found anything that looks even a little like a plant fossil.

DEXTER: (*quietly*) I know there are no plants on Mars *now.* But I think this rock tells us that once, long ago, there *were* plants on Mars. Maybe they lived underwater here. Either way, one of them left its imprint on this rock long before anybody arrived here from Earth.

MR. REYNOLDS: (*helplessly*) Well, Dr. Kang says it's impossible, kids. I don't know what else we can say. Sorry for taking up your time, Dr. Kang. Let's go.

MRS. REYNOLDS: (*firmly*) I know where I found that rock, Dr. Kang. I think you should consider the possibility that Dexter actually found a fossil.

DEXTER: Look at the rock, Dr. Kang. Have you ever seen a rock like that on Earth?

DR. KANG: (*Holds rock half.*) Well, no, not exactly. It looks like some of those rocks that the space **rover** found here back in 2005. Still, how can this be true? If it is true . . .

RITA: It changes everything!

Dr. Kang: (*Faces the family.*) It does. It changes everything we know or thought we knew about Mars. That is why I am having such a hard time with this.

Mr. Reynolds: Me too. I'm having a hard time believing that my boy found something that nobody else ever found.

Dr. Kang: (*not really listening*) Well, he's a smart boy. Now listen, Dexter. I need to do some research and check out your rock **thoroughly**. Maybe it's the greatest discovery ever made on Mars. Maybe it's nothing at all. Will you let me keep your rock? A lot of scientists will want to study this fossil, if that's what it really is. And we'll want to keep it very safe so the evidence doesn't wear away.

Dexter: Well . . .

Mrs. Reynolds: (*sharply*) Dexter!

Dexter: Okay, fine. It's not really one of my favorites, anyway.

Dr. Kang: Not one of your favorites? I see. Let me see what I can find out. This will be very interesting. (*She exits.*)

RITA: Not one of your favorites? Dexter, you are so weird.

DEXTER: Well, it isn't. My favorite is the one with the rose-colored . . .

RITA: (*Rolls her eyes.*) Dexter, honestly, who cares?

MR. REYNOLDS: I'm so proud. I must have seen about a million rocks break at the mines, and not a single one had a fossil inside. When Dexter breaks his first rock, he makes a major scientific discovery!

MRS. REYNOLDS: Dexter was pretty lucky. But he was also careful. He looks closely at every rock. The scientists will all be amazed to hear that he found a fossil. For now, let's go have a nice dinner at home. (*They exit.*)

ACT 2, SCENE 2: Dexter's home

(A month has gone by. RITA *is standing in the kitchen.* DEXTER *is sorting a pile of rocks on the kitchen table. As their mother enters, he sweeps all but one into a box beside him on the floor.)*

MRS. REYNOLDS: Hi, honey. Is your homework done?

DEXTER: (*Holds the rock.*) Yes. Mom, did you see the spaceship?

RITA: (*enters*) I hear there were 50 more scientists on board. Dr. Kang has had people coming from Earth all week long.

MRS. REYNOLDS: Half of the scientists are in the mines. They are down in Zone 3 where I found your rock. They're digging through the formations and trying to find more rocks like yours.

DEXTER: Are they cracking *all* the rocks open?

RITA: How else will they find fossils, Dexter? They have to look inside the rocks.

MRS. REYNOLDS: Well, I'm sure they don't have to crack every single rock, honey.

RITA: Oh, that's true. They probably have special tools that can look right through the rocks.

DEXTER: (*Turns his rock over.*) I'd love a tool like that. Maybe then I could get a better look at this rock. Mom brought it home from a new section of Zone 3. It has a bunch of colorful layers and a tiny dark shape at the bottom.

MR. REYNOLDS: (*enters*) Hey, Dexter! Dr. Kang sent a nice message to me at work today. She told me that the fossil scientists are very impressed with your discovery. They're even calling it the Reynolds fossil!

MRS. REYNOLDS: Do you hear that, Dexter? You're famous!

RITA: We're all famous if they're calling it the Reynolds fossil. Maybe they should call it the Dexter Reynolds fossil.

DEXTER: (*Still distracted by the rock.*) That's okay. I don't mind.

MR. REYNOLDS: Of course he doesn't mind. Everybody knows who discovered that fossil. And even if they find a million more fossils, Dexter's is still the first.

RITA: Your silly rocks weren't so silly after all, Dexter.

DEXTER: (*Looks at his rock through the magnifying glass.*) Oh, they're not silly. Each rock might tell us something new about Mars. Even the little shape on this rock might . . . Hey! Do you know what this looks like? I think it's a tiny feather!

MRS. REYNOLDS: (*Walks over to* DEXTER.) Are you sure? Let me see.

RITA: (*sighs*) I'll call Dr. Kang . . .

Focus Question: How might space be a part of our future?

A Check Understanding ★

Using ideas from the selection, make a list of the ways space may be a part of our future. Do you think these events will happen? PRACTICE COMPANION 359

B Understand Literary Elements ★★

A motive is the reason why a character does something. Motives tell you what a character wants. What is Dexter's motive for collecting rocks? What does this tell you about his character? Discuss your answers with a partner.

C Share and Compare ★★

With a partner, compare your list of the ways space may be a part of our future. How does your partner's list differ from yours? How is it the same?

D Think Critically ★★★★

Why do people study space? Use examples from the selection to explain.

Why do people study space?

Use these activities to show what you've learned about the theme question.

1. Imagine that you discovered a new constellation. Design your own model of it.
2. Draw your constellation on black construction paper. Cut out small holes for stars to form the shape of the constellation.
3. Shine a light behind the paper to see the shape that the stars would make in the sky.

1. With a partner, design two Web pages about space and space exploration. Include the text and pictures that you want on your Web pages.
2. Present your Web page designs to the class.

1. Choose your favorite selection from the unit. Tell your group why you chose it.
2. Read your favorite part aloud.
3. Search for other books about space to read and share.

1. Imagine that your town is located on the moon.
2. Write a story that describes your daily life. Think about how life on the moon is different from the life you live on Earth. Be sure to include dialogue between characters.
3. Read your story to a friend.

Glossary

Pronunciation Key

a	**bat**	oi	**toy**
ā	**ape**	ou	sh**out**
air	**air**	ŏŏ	b**oo**k
ä	**par**k	ōō	m**oo**n
e	**le**t	s	**s**un
ē	**eas**y	sh	pre**ss**ure
i	**if**	th	**th**e, **th**ing
ī	**lie**	u	n**u**t
îr	**dear**	ûr	c**ir**cle
k	**c**ause	ə	**a**go
o	**lo**t	ər	moth**er**
ō	**go**	′	primary stress
ô	**all**	′	secondary stress

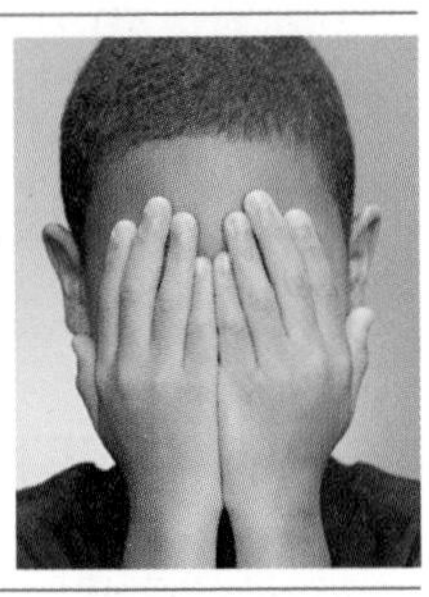

ashamed (ə shāmd′) *adj.* feeling upset or guilty;
Jean felt ashamed after he spoke sharply to his friend. **84**

binary (bī′ nə rē) *adj.* having two parts;
The two bright lights told scientists they had found a binary star system. **24**

browse (brouz) *v.* to look over casually or skim;
I like to browse through a book before I buy it. **67**

complain (kəm plān′) *v.* to find fault with something or to express discontent;
My cousins always complain about their birthday gifts. **87**

complicated (kom′ pli kā′ tid) *adj.* complex, difficult to understand;
Although there were only four ingredients, the complicated instructions made the recipe quite difficult. **18**

compound (kom′ pound′) *n.* a fenced-in group of buildings;
The army compound has barracks, offices, and a garage. **81**

console (kən sōl′) *v.* to comfort someone or make them feel better;
Dad tried to console my sister after she scraped her knee. **64**

crave (krāv) *v.* to want greatly;
On a hot summer day, I crave an ice-cold drink. **36**

devote (di vōt′) *v.* to give time and effort to something;
Our study group will devote every Saturday this month to preparing for the debate competition. **16**

ellipse (i lips′) *n.* an oval;
The track was shaped like an ellipse; it reminded me of an egg. **37**

factor (fak′ tər) *n.* an ingredient or element that affects a decision;
The weather was one factor in deciding if we should go hiking. **47**

formation (fôr mā′ shən) *n.* something that is made, arranged, or formed, as in a pattern;
We arranged the bowling pins in their correct formation. **58**

gravity (gra′ vi tē) *n.* the force that pulls things toward Earth;
Gravity is what makes a glass hit the floor when it falls from your hand. **23**

grind (grīnd) *v.* to make something smooth by rubbing it against a rough surface;
Rock collectors use a special wheel to grind and polish the surface of rocks until they are smooth and shiny. **13**

identify (ī den′ tə fī′) *v.* to tell exactly who or what a person or thing is;
Detectives might use fingerprints to identify a criminal. **19**

imprint (im′ print′) *n.* a mark made by pressing;
When I slept on my hands, you could see an imprint of my fingers on my cheek. **93**

inaccurate (in ak′ yər it) *adj.* not correct;
The inaccurate information on the map made us get lost. **38**

lunar (lo͞o′ nər) *adj.* having to do with the moon;
There are hills and craters on the lunar surface. **30**

magnificent (mag ni′ fə sənt) *adj.* very grand and beautiful;
The queen wore a magnificent crown with many beautiful rubies and diamonds on it. **63**

marvel (mär′ vəl) *v.* to feel a sense of wonder or astonishment;
People continue to marvel at the wonders of modern technology. **76**

miserable (miz′ rə bəl) *adj.* being in a state of unhappiness;
We had a miserable time on the picnic because there were so many bees. **64**

module (moj′ ōōl) *n.* an independent vehicle that is part of a large space vehicle;
We watched a film about the first trip of the moon-landing module. **74**

option (op′ shən) *n.* a choice;
One lunch option in the cafeteria is a salad with turkey. **73**

perch (pûrch) *n.* a raised place for resting, sitting, or standing;
The bird sits on a perch. **19**

philosopher (fi los′ ə fər) *n.* a thinker, or a person who seeks and speaks about wisdom;
A philosopher might have had many students who wanted to learn from his or her experiences and studies. **33**

previously (prē′ vē əs lē) *adv.* happening before;
James and I went to the store previously, but forgot to buy the milk. **34**

professionally (prə fesh′ ə nəl lē) *adv.* in a way that shows ability or training;
I would like to dance professionally and maybe work on Broadway. **10**

proof (prōōf) *n.* evidence or facts showing that something is true;
We have no proof that the catfish ate the goldfish. **52**

reflect (ri flekt′) *v.* to give back, bounce off;
A car's mirrors reflect the images of the vehicles behind it. **12**

revolve (ri volv′) *v.* to move in a circle around a center point;
The little children hold hands and revolve in a circle around a child who is standing in the center. **14**

rotate (rō′ tāt) *v.* to turn on an axis;
The chickens rotate in the big ovens behind the deli counter at the store. **11**

rover (rō′ vər) *n.* a vehicle for exploring the surface of a planet or other object in space;
The rover picked up many rocks from the planet's surface. **96**

scramble (skram′ bəl) *v.* to move quickly, especially on all fours;
We had to scramble on the floor to scoop up all the glass marbles that fell out of the vase. **85**

slender (slen′ dər) *adj.* narrow or thin;
A slender ribbon was tied around the girl's straw hat. **75**

sphere (sfîr) *n.* a round shape, like a ball;
A basketball is a sphere, but a football is not. **32**

survey (sûr′ vā′) *n.* a study or a broad look at something;
We used pictures taken from a plane to do a survey of the types of houses in our town. **14**

tackle (tak′ əl) *v.* to deal with;
Mom and I will tackle all the laundry on Sunday afternoon. **60**

telescope (te′ lə skōp′) *n.* an instrument that makes faraway objects seem larger and closer;
We use the telescope to watch the shooting stars on a summer night. **7**

thoroughly (thûr′ ō lē) *adv.* completely;
I checked my homework thoroughly before I handed it in. **97**

undeserved (un′ di zûrvd′) *adj.* not worthy of;
The movie received undeserved criticism. **56**

verge (vûrj) *n.* the point of which something is about to occur;
The frightened toddler was on the verge of crying. **62**

zone (zōn) *n.* a region or area that is separate from another area or has a special quality;
City Hall has a no-parking zone all around the outside of the building. **94**

Index

P

S

T

U

V

Acknowledgments

Photo Credits: Cover ©Digital Stock/Corbis; **4** ©Digital Stock/Corbis; **5** (tl) ©Alamy Images, (tr) ©Leda_d/Shutterstock, (bl) ©Comstock Images/Alamy, (br) ©NASA; **6** ©Victoria Art Gallery, Bath and North East Somerset Council/Bridgeman Art Library; (thru-out bkgd) ©Photodisc/Getty Images; **8** ©Artville/Getty Images; **14–15** (bkgd) ©NASA; **16** ©SSPL/The Image Works; **18–19** ©Royal Astronomical Society/Photo Researchers, Inc.; **20–21** ©Digital Stock/Corbis; **22–23** ©NASA/Corbis; **24** ©NASA; **26** ©The Granger Collection, New York; **27** ©ImageState/AGE Fotostock; **28** ©NASA/Corbis; **29** (l) ©Leda_d/Shutterstock, (r) ©Alamy Images; **30–31** ©StockTrek/Getty Images; **32–51** (bkgd) ©StockTrek/Getty Images; **32** Public Domain/NNDB.com; **33** ©The Print Collector/Alamy; **34** ©Hulton Archive/Getty Images; **35** ©Jody Dole/The Image Bank/Getty Images; **36** ©Brand X Pictures/Punchstock; **37** ©Hulton Archive/Getty Images; **38** ©Stefano Bianchetti/Corbis; **39** ©Jupiter Images/Getty Images; **40–41** ©Photodisc/Getty Images; **43** (t) ©The Granger Collection, New York, (b) ©The Granger Collection, New York; **44** ©Science Source/Photo Researchers; **45** ©David A. Hardy/Photo Researchers, Inc.; **46** (bkgrd) ©Comstock Select/Corbis; **47** ©Digital Stock/Corbis; **48–49** ©Stocktrek Images/Alamy Images; **50** ©Space Frontiers/Hulton Archive/Getty Images; **52–53** ©Digital Stock/Corbis; **54** ©Photodisc/Getty Images; **55** (t) ©NASA, (b) ©Comstock Images/Alamy; **79** (t) ©Brand X Pictures/PunchStock, (b) ©Pixtal/Agefotostock.

Art Credits: 8–9 ©The McGraw-Hill Companies, Inc./Leah Palmer Preiss; **10–11**, **12–13**, **25** ©The McGraw-Hill Companies, Inc./Leah Palmer Preiss; **56–78** ©The McGraw-Hill Companies, Inc./Zues Bacon; **81–103** ©The McGraw-Hill Companies, Inc./Colin Mier.